PELICAN BOOKS

ANIMAL CAMOUFLAGE

BY

E. M. STEPHENSON

M.Sc., F.Z.S.

in collaboration with

CHARLES STEWART

PUBLISHED BY

PENGUIN BOOKS

HARMONDSWORTH MIDDLESEX ENGLAND

245 FIFTH AVENUE NEW YORK U.S.A.

First published 1946

"Formed by the eye, and therefore, like the eye,
Full of strange shapes, of habits, and of forms,
Varying in subjects as the eye doth roll
To every varied object in his glance."

Love's Labour's Lost,
Act. V. Sc. ii.

MADE AND PRINTED IN GREAT BRITAIN FOR PENGUIN BOOKS LIMITED,
BY RICHARD CLAY AND COMPANY, LTD., BUNGAY, SUFFOLK.

COLLOGRAVURE PLATES PRINTED IN GREAT BRITAIN BY HARRISON AND SONS LTD.
44–47, ST. MARTIN'S LANE, LONDON, W.C.2, PRINTERS TO H.M. THE KING.

HISTORICAL PREFACE AND ACKNOWLEDGMENTS

The ancients were familiar with the colour changes of the chameleon and the octopus, and of fish such as the mullet which were bred in fish-ponds for gastronomic purposes. From Greek and Roman times until about two centuries ago further examples of colour change do not seem to have attracted attention.

The first recorded observations that frogs and toads change colour are those of Vallisnieri (1751) and Roesel von Rosenhof (1758). The varying tints of the chameleon prawn were described by Kröyer in 1842. Insects were next added to the list, and during the last few years examples of colour change have been found within the Annelid group—namely, in leeches and in the larval stages of bristle worms and in the Mollusca. Thus colour change (by means of pigments moving within special pigment cells) is of widespread occurrence in the animal kingdom. There are many examples both among the lower Vertebrates and four in major groups of the Invertebrates.

Early in the nineteenth century observations on this subject were followed by investigation into the means by which colour change was effected. Cuvier was perhaps the first to suggest an explanation. In 1819 Sangiovanni correctly observed the behaviour of pigment cells in cephalopods, and named the cells chromatophores. Milne-Edwards in 1834 gave the first correct description and interpretation of the chromatophores in reptiles. During the second half of the nineteenth century pioneer work on the subject of colour change gave place to more accurate and intensive research. For many years the only factors governing the chromatophores were thought to be the nervous system and the direct action of the environment. When the existence of hormones was established, the possibility that they might constitute an additional factor arose, and in 1898 Corona and Moroni found that if adrenalin entered the circulation of the frog it had a strong effect on the chromatophores of this animal.

From 1900 onwards, many hundreds of scientific papers have appeared on the subject of colour change, from workers in various countries. Much interesting work was done on Crustacea early in the century by Professors Keeble and Gamble, and on frogs and lizards by Professor G. H. Parker. Professor Parker may be said to have established an American school of studies in colour change, from which much work has continued to emerge up to the present day.

An important milestone was reached in 1922 by the discovery by Hogben and Winton of the action of the pituitary secretion on the chromatophores of frogs. This began a series of researches published over a number of years by Professor Hogben and others collaborating with him, entitled "The Pigmentary Effector System." Professor L. T. Hogben leads the English school of studies in colour change, and to him is due the introduction of methods which allow for complete accuracy in recording observations and controlling experimental conditions. His introduction of graphs showing the time-curves of colour changes makes it possible to distinguish rapid effects due to nerve control from slower effects due to hormone control. The analytical study of the eye as a receptor peculiar to each type of animal has also contributed to the solution of the problems concerned.

Hogben's school works mainly with Vertebrates. The major steps in discovering the mechanism controlling colour change in Crustacea were taken by Perkins, working in America, and Koller working in Germany, both publishing independently in 1928. The position was further clarified by H. G. Smith, working under Hogben, in 1938.

Colour change is a special aspect of the whole concept of Animal Camouflage. The details of its mechanism, and the physiology involved, belong, however, to the laboratory, while animal camouflage is essentially a field study. It may be assumed that naturalists in every age, the world over, have noticed examples of colour harmony, mimicry and so forth. The stimulus to explore, collect and classify, set in motion by Linnaeus, no doubt directed attention to the subject on a wider scale. But careful investigation of the matter, and theories concerning it, are of very recent date, and originate in the work of the explorer-naturalists of the nineteenth century—Wallace, Darwin, Thayer, Bates and Müller. Among the manifold adaptive characters of animals, adaptive coloration became singled out almost as a subject apart. Much speculation took place on how it came about and to what extent it favoured survival. Theories of adaptive coloration were later taken to extreme lengths by some writers, and were in consequence discredited.

The most recent contribution to the subject comes from Dr. Hugo B. Cott's *Adaptive Coloration in Animals*. The author, who combines the knowledge of an academic zoologist with that of a widely travelled naturalist, clearly portrays the optico–physiological principles employed in nature, and gives a critical review of recent work bearing on the subject. From this rich field I have drawn many examples and illustrations.

I owe much to some years spent in the live atmosphere of Professor Munro Fox's department, and to his interest in animal physiology. I also had the privilege of a brief spell of work under Professor Hogben, in connection with my research on colour change in Crustacea. I owe direction towards the physical aspects of the subject, and its philosophical significance, to my collaborator Mr. Charles Stewart, who also drew my attention to such works as those of P. D. Ouspensky. I am indebted to Miss S. M. Richards, B.Sc., and to Miss C. Lucas, M.Sc., for reading the manuscript and making valuable comments, and to the latter for providing several essential references.

E. M. STEPHENSON.

CONTENTS

LIST OF PLATES
(*between pp.* 96 *and* 97)

The drawings appearing in the text as line diagrams are acknowledged to the following: Figure 2, *the Author*. Figure 4, *after Poulton by courtesy of the Linnaean Society*. Figures 3, 5 and 6, *W. S. Bristowe by courtesy of The Ray Society*.

ANIMAL CAMOUFLAGE

CHAPTER I

THE NATURE OF CAMOUFLAGE

MEANING AND DEFINITION OF CAMOUFLAGE

CAMOUFLAGE is a strange word to have come into everyday use; yet a special term was needed to cover this curious art that modern man has rediscovered on such a large scale. Disguise, make-believe, effacement, mimicry—all these word-meanings are connected with the idea of camouflage. The word itself does not seem to be a very old one. Parisian slang has *camoufler*, to disguise, apparently connected with the older *camouflet*, an old form of asphyxiating mine used for military purposes, to blow smoke in the face of an enemy.

MAIN TYPES OF CAMOUFLAGE

Camouflage takes many forms. It may be simple disguise involving the accurate copying of a harmless object, such as a rock or a leaf. For the purposes of bluff it may involve the weak putting on the appearance of the strong, or the reverse. Another type of camouflage is the breaking up of the true outline of an object such as a factory until it merges with its general surroundings—the camouflage of effacement; or the object, while contrasting with its surroundings, may be made to present an appearance which has no significance to the mind of the observer. For example, the long roof of a building may be made to present the appearance of a number of irregular areas none of which can be recognised as any known architectural form. Camouflage artists *may* make objects look so strange that their disguise draws attention to them and makes them conspicuous, but this is due to imperfect understanding of the art, and defeats its own end. Again, a building or an animal may be revealed by the shape of the shadow it casts, and effacement or breaking-up of such a shadow is a most important aspect of camouflage.

Recently the camouflage of effacement has become of vital importance, especially as a disguise from enemies in the air. Camouflage of this kind is an exacting art and must comply strictly with certain conditions. The more nearly it resembles the camouflage found in nature the more successful does it prove, for in nature the art of camouflage attains perfection, and man's efforts are often clumsy and imperfect by comparison.

Except in the camouflage of inanimate objects, appearance is only one of the factors called into play. In the case of a living animal it may be assisted by posture, gesture, action, and even sound, all increasing the effectiveness of the initial appearance. Among the many kinds of insects camouflaged as leaves, there are some, such as the mantis, which from time to time make irregular swaying movements like those of a leaf caught by a random breath of air. A spider that " mimics " an ant always zigzags from side to side in its walk, after the manner of an ant, and holds up its second pair of legs in front of its head, keeping them in constant vibration like the ant's antennae. On the other hand, perfect stillness may be the cue, as in the case of insects resembling sticks and stones.

Man's Copying of Nature

Many of the tricks of camouflage are old secrets of the stage or of the conjuror. The actor must both look and act his part. A soldier camouflaged as a corn-sheaf must not sneeze !

One of man's earliest uses of camouflage is found in the old-time boar-traps, which were pits covered across the top with branches. The art of the trapper involves accurate placing of the materials covering the trap. The hunters tried to make the trap invisible by matching the covering with the surrounding ground, thus consciously achieving a result such as nature often brings about unconsciously.

Disguise is also a very early form of camouflage. In the Trois Frères Cave, in France, is a wall-painting of Palaeolithic man disguised as a reindeer.* When approaching a herd of bison, which has no fear of a solitary wolf, a North American Indian clothes himself in a wolf-skin and moves like a wolf. Various primitive peoples when hunting disguise themselves as animals. African Bushmen wear the head and hide of a hartebeest over their shoulders, and mimic the movement of that animal when they hunt elephants. When stalking ostrich they use an ostrich disguise, carrying the head of one of these birds on the end of a long, pliant stick, which they move in suitable ways, while keeping their bodies concealed.

---

* Illustration described as " Prehistoric Sorcerer," *Mysteries and Secrets of Magic*, C. J. S. Thompson, p. 70. John Lane, The Bodley Head, Ltd.

THE MEANING OF CAMOUFLAGE IN NATURE

We must first make clear one important point. When we speak of camouflage in nature we refer to certain effects seen through the human eye and judged by the human brain. Just how things appear to the eyes of animals we shall never know, though the more closely they resemble us in their general make-up the more probable is it that they see things somewhat as we do. It is certain that many animals recognise their own kind by sight, and distinguish human beings or natural enemies. The use of decoys in duck-shooting is based on this fact. The success of primitive hunting disguises points in the same direction. There is also ample evidence that animals recognise suitable food by sight and avoid dangerous and distasteful prey—witness the art of the fly fisherman. We shall consider this question carefully later, but for the moment let us assume that camouflage plays the same rôle of concealment among the higher animals as it does in the human world. A grass snake moving in search of prey fails to notice a frog that squats motionless, blending perfectly with the grass. A yellow spider crouching on a dandelion flower captures the unsuspecting hover fly as it alights to feed.

Camouflage is found on a very large scale in the world of nature. Conspicuous animals are far outnumbered by the host of those to be seen only by chance or by a trained observer. Hunting animals are camouflaged nearly as often as the creatures on which they prey, as in the case of the white winter fur of both hare and fox in snowy regions. The more we look into this curious state of affairs, the more intriguing does it become. In the end it leads us deep into the search to understand why living things are coloured as we find them, why they behave as we observe them to do.

METHODS BY WHICH CAMOUFLAGE IS EFFECTED

The effect of concealment is brought about in various ways. Suppose you have dropped a glove in the garden and go to look for it. In your mind's eye you hold a picture of the glove with palm and five fingers. If the glove has fallen flat it will not be difficult to find, but if it has fallen in some strange position you may fail to see it because the familiar outline is missing. So the first principle of camouflage is to do away with the outline.

Your glove is a solid object, and as you see it lying on the table you notice that the upper parts are well lighted while the lower parts are in shade. If you had to draw a glove on paper you would put in its outline and then add shading to make it look solid. If you look round the room you realise how greatly the solid effect of objects depends on the form of their shading. If we can see but not handle an object, nothing but its shading tells us whether it is flat or solid. So a second principle of camouflage is to do away with the shading that makes an object or an animal look solid. Some shapes cast a minimum of shadow. We have the example of a pole or rod which sticks out at the back of a lorry towards the oncomer and casts no shadow, so that he walks or drives right into it, or a stake in the garden, seen from above when the sun is high, which spikes the gardener in the eye as he stoops down.

Light not only causes shadows to play on the object itself, revealing its shape and texture, but also casts a shadow on the background. If an animal's body casts a tell-tale shadow, it can be recognised at once, just as a person can be identified by his shadow cast on a

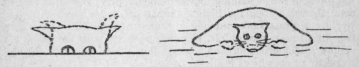

FIG. 1.—Diagrams of cat in concealment attitudes (Examples of form camouflage.) (a) Rising slowly to look over a ledge, ears flattened. (b) Crouched in a position that minimises shadow and obscures shape of head.

blind. So a third principle of camouflage is the effacement or disguise of the shadow.

Colour harmony is a self-evident need in camouflage. Khaki replaced the soldier's red coat for a practical reason. Many of the tartans of the Scotch clans made a perfect colour blend with the moorland scenery and were invaluable for concealment and for ambush. Heather mixtures and earth browns are the only possible wear for game-shooting and deer-stalking. A bird-watcher would never dream of wearing light clothes. A casual visitor to the countryside sees no wild life except perhaps for rabbits, a few bright insects, and birds on the wing. This is typical for Britain and most of Europe, where nearly all the wild life that survives wears sober colourings; and it holds for wild life over the greater part of the world.

If, then, we consider a camouflaged animal in its natural setting, the effect is found to result from one or more of these conditions: the natural outline is broken up or blurred; the shading which would reveal a solid body, bent limbs, and so on is absent; the shadow cast on the ground is concealed; there is harmony of colour and tone.

The *natural outline* is disguised by spots, stripes, or irregular patches of some colour which contrasts strongly with the general ground colour of the animal. These marks or patterns catch the observer's eye, distract his attention, and suggest unreal forms which do not suggest to him anything living. In "How the Leopard got his Spots" Kipling expresses the idea in his own way. "Now you *are* a beauty!" said the Ethiopian. "You can lie out on the bare ground and look like a heap of pebbles. You can lie out on the naked rocks and look like a piece of pudding stone. You can lie out on a leafy branch and look like sunshine sifting through the leaves; and you can lie right across the centre of a path and look like nothing in particular. Think of that and purr!" Biologists call this effect "disruptive coloration"; when used for purposes of warfare it goes by the name of "dazzle camouflage". It is clearly a form of optical illusion.

The effect of *natural shading* is countered by a simple device known as "counter-shading". If a toy animal coloured fawn all over is placed out of doors, light from the sky makes its back look pale, its underside dark, and its flanks various shades of fawn between pale and dark. It stands out clearly in relief and looks very solid. In nature, a fawn-coloured animal's back is of darker colour, its under parts are very pale fawn or white, and its flanks grade from dark above to pale fawn lower down. The result is an even tone of fawn all over, making the animal appear flat instead of solid—again an optical illusion. Against a background of the same tone it would escape notice. *Concealment of shadow* is effected by the animal pressing itself close against the ground or taking up special positions which will be described later. *Colour harmony* consists in an accurate matching in tint, hue, or shade between the animal and the vegetation, stones, or ground on which it rests.

Many creatures, as we shall see later, lack a colour sense. It may be asked of what use is colour harmony, or the colours which contribute to counter-shading, in the case of such animals. The answer is quite clear; a photograph of an animal in its natural setting shows just as much concealment as would a colour plate, for there is matching in tone and shade. To those that can see colour the effect is different, but not more complete.

STILLNESS AS AN AID TO CONCEALMENT

The effects of camouflage are usually at their best when the animal is still. Numbers of creatures remain motionless throughout the daylight hours, and move and feed only at night. Of these, some hide themselves, but many rest in exposed positions, escaping destruction only because they so closely resemble their surroundings. There are the strange " stick " caterpillars found among ivy or on the twigs of many kinds of forest tree. We might never know of their existence unless we happened to pick foliage on which they rested. In shape, colour, and position they exactly resemble leafless twigs or dead leaf-stalks. Night-flying moths rest on bark, palings, and so on, resembling them perfectly in colour and markings. Unless they are disturbed and move we do not know that they are there. We might say much the same of the all-too-inconspicuous clothes moth.

When our cabbages are riddled with holes and we go over them in search of caterpillars, it is easy enough to find the hairy yellow-and-black kind that turn into the large Cabbage White butterfly. But the caterpillar of the small Cabbage White, which eats right into the heart of the cabbage, may be staring us in the face the whole time without our seeing it. This caterpillar rests on the upper side of the leaf, stretched motionless along the pale midrib, and fully exposed. It is exactly like the leaf in colour, and has a soft, velvety texture that resembles the waxy bloom on the cabbage.

Most of us would never see a frog or a toad unless its hopping or crawling caught our attention. It is easy enough to look straight at a bird sitting on her nest without knowing she is there at all. How complete the combined effect of camouflage and stillness can be is shown by a passage from Major Cheesman's book *In Unknown Arabia*: " I was anxious to photograph the nest of the Houbara; * and thought that by flying trained falcons over the ground one might induce the sitting birds to show fight and thus give away the position of the nest. We covered a lot of ground and knew we had passed many sitting hens, because the cocks were frequently seen grouped together. Yet the hawks failed to discover a single nest, and we, quartering the ground carefully, were equally unsuccessful." Yet the eye of the falcon is among the keenest in the world.

If you ever go shrimping, you know how difficult it is to see the shrimps on the bottom of a sandy pool until you disturb them. And you can stand on a small flat fish without suspecting it until it betrays its presence by squirming from beneath your foot. Such examples could be multiplied without end.

Many animals, however, must go about their business in daylight and risk being seen while they are on the move. If they are alarmed

* A large bird rather like a bustard.

or suspect danger they may do one of two things: bolt into cover or "freeze" into stillness. When still, their pursuer may pass them by, or he may be baffled for a few seconds, allowing the quarry to start off again and make good its escape. Quite a number of animals if disturbed sham death or "play possum"—a phrase which comes from the performance of the opossum, an animal rather like a cat, but with a narrow, pointed head and an almost hairless tail, a native of the northern States of the U.S.A. When in danger the opossum becomes rigid, with closed eyes and generally shrunken appearance, as though it has been dead for some hours. This is a very successful way of escape, for animals that feed on living prey will not eat carrion. A homely instance of the same thing is the spider. When disturbed, it rolls on its back, draws up its legs and looks quite dead. It will allow itself to be pushed and poked and still give no sign of life.

Defenceless creatures such as frogs and small lizards often owe their safety to this habit of stillness in moments of danger. The squatting instinct is very strong in young plovers exposed on shingle beaches without cover, and in game-birds on the sparse vegetation of a moor. At the danger signal of a passing shadow, which may mean the swoop of some bird of prey, or at a warning cry from the mother bird, these chicks flatten themselves against the ground and remain completely still. It is then almost impossible to find them. Mountain sheep and deer remain like statues in moments of danger. Not unless they know they are discovered will they run the risk of movement.

Some examples of camouflage considered more carefully will teach us more on the subject.

The photograph of woodcock chicks, newly hatched (Plate 2), is a perfect example of natural outline concealed by patches of strongly contrasting colours. The eye is caught by these irregular patches, similar in tone to light patches of dead leaves and dark earth on the woodland floor, especially to the dappled patches of bright light and deep shade cast by the leafy canopy above. The chicks crouch close against the ground and cast no shadow.

In looking at this photograph we start with a big advantage—we know the chicks are there. If the area of the photograph were as big as the floor of a room it might be hours before we spotted the little patch of chicks. Mr. Hugh B. Cott, the photographer, knew there were nests with chicks in this wood, and knew just what to look for. But he could find nothing. Just as the quest seemed hopeless a mother woodcock flew up from the ground. No chicks were disclosed, but, feeling carefully over the spot she had left, the warm fluffiness of the little birds revealed them to his touch.

In the photograph of the bush buck (Plate 1) we have a beautiful glimpse of camouflage in an African forest. The shade is deep, for strong light filters down through the dense foliage of tall trees. We notice the delicate tones of the animal's coat—its slightly darkened back, the pale but not white underparts. In the rather dim lighting of the forest there is no strong relief of light and shade, and no strong counter-shading is required. Here and there a vivid spot or fleck of sunlight finds its way to the undergrowth or to the forest floor. A few white spots on the buck's coat help to complete the insubstantial and elusive appearance of the animal and to blend it with its forest background. It could escape recognition at least for a few seconds, and that brief delay might be of great advantage. It could be gone while a leopard crouched to spring or a hunter raised rifle to shoulder.

Probably it never occurs to us that the zebra's conspicuous stripes are a most finished style of camouflage. Herds of zebra are very easily seen by day in the open country or scrub of their native home, but in daylight they have little to fear from their enemies. Fleet of foot, with most acute senses of sight, hearing, and smell, they are among the most wary and most difficult to approach of all wild game. Many a hunter and animal photographer has been fascinated by their elusiveness.

In the twilight of dusk and dawn zebras are very liable to attack from lions and leopards, and it is at these hours that the zebras become almost invisible. The black and white stripes blend into an elusive light grey, the grey of ground and vegetation at such an hour. The outline of the animal melts away, for the dark stripes cut right across the outer contour at every part of the body. On the underparts, which would tend to be shaded and rather darker in colour, the stripes are much narrower, while on the upper lighted parts the stripes are broad. So the bulky body, instead of looking solid by reason of natural shadows, appears flat.

A noted hunter tells how at dusk he cautiously approached some thin cover in which a herd of zebra was known to be located. With him were keen-eyed natives experienced in zebra hunting. They crept to within 40 or 50 yards of the herd, which stood motionless. Even at that distance no one could descry a single animal, so perfectly did they merge with the twilight grey of the scenery.

The striking nature of the zebra's camouflage is but one instance of many. It is effective only at the right place and time—in the zebra's natural home and during the half lights. When we look at the camouflage of any animal we must also picture the scenery and lighting of the stage on which it is naturally exposed. In Guiana there live bats with pure white fur. Were they to spend the day in hollow trees or other dark crannies, after the manner of British bats, they would be seen and killed. Instead, they hang in the open from the leaves of palm trees. These leaves look bright and silvery from beneath, and so does the white fur of the sleeping bats.

Among the coral reefs where the sea floor is a brilliantly lit garden of glowing colours, a drab-coloured animal would show up like a dark glove on a flower-bed. But vividly coloured fishes seem part of the garden itself, and the gentle rippling of their fins resembles seaweed swaying with the movement of the water.

What a difference the right background can make even to the familiar robin ! Hopping in the snow, it is a real Christmas Card robin, its red breast brightly displayed. Now it flits to the sheltered side of the hedge . . . and disappears. Surely you saw the robin perch there? You move gently towards the place where it settled. Suddenly your mind interprets what your eyes are seeing—that dull crimson leaf among the bare twigs is the robin itself, sitting quite still and looking straight at you. Its brown head and wings merge into the brown of the hedge, its beak, seen end on, is a mere dot, its legs the slenderest of dead stems. No one would suggest that a robin needs camouflage, for it is a bird very capable of looking after itself. But the fact remains that it is not a conspicuous bird when seen in its country setting. This may explain why many people who know robins from pictures say they have never seen the bird itself.

Most of the examples just described are of disruptive or dazzle camouflage in animals with black-and-white or rather sober colourings. An example of delicate colour harmonies is found in the caterpillar of the Privet Hawk Moth. This creature's colour scheme is of special interest, since it spends most of its life upside down, and is counter-shaded in a way the reverse of the usual.

Caterpillars of the Privet Hawk Moth are bulky, pale green creatures, about two inches long when fully grown. When they are noticed it is generally in the early autumn, when they are crawling in purposeful fashion along the ground, making for some patch of deep loose earth in which they can burrow, to turn into a chrysalis and shelter for the winter. But in the summer weeks when the caterpillars grow and feed among the privet leaves they are very difficult to see.

To an observer looking down on a privet hedge the caterpillar is hidden by the leaves. Its danger comes from hunters looking upwards—for instance, blue tits swinging on the stems. Stand beside a privet hedge and look up at the young shoots near the top; here are the most tender leaves, the caterpillar's chosen feeding place. Each privet leaf slants upwards from the stem and is partly folded like a half-opened book, so you see numbers of pale green leaf-profiles. The white midrib of each leaf stands out clearly like the back of the book, and light shines down through the pale side veins.

Now that your eyes are used to the look of the privet leaves themselves, you can begin to search for something that looks like an extra leaf, rather more narrow than the others. If you find this —the caterpillar—you see a round-bodied insect so skilfully coloured that it passes for the profile of a thin leaf with light shining through it. The caterpillar clasps the stem with its tail end and leans back, upside down, making the same angle with the stem as do the leaves, or it may stretch its body under the midrib of the leaf. It remains straight and still for most of the daylight hours, feeding and moving about for the most part under cover of darkness; in any case the greater part of its daylight life is spent in an upside-down position.

The caterpillar's lighted upper surface is privet-leaf green, and so are the sides of its body. Its back, which is more in shadow, is a pale yellow-green, so that when shaded it appears the same colour as the rest of the body. Thus a dark under-shadow, which would betray a solid rounded body, is avoided, and the body appears flat. Along the caterpillar's sides are white stripes, each with a purple stripe alongside. These stripes are the same distance apart and at the same angle as the side veins of the leaf. The purple line appears as a shadow throwing the white " vein " into relief. Between the stripes are pinkish-purple areas over the green ground-colour; the effect is just like the delicately shaded areas of the leaf that lie between the veins.

If you look at the caterpillar by itself, away from its natural setting, you see a conspicuous solid animal with certain colours on its skin. If you see it on a summer's day hanging under its leaf, with green light shining upon it through the leaves,* the creature appears not only flat but almost transparent, its surface traversed by pale vein-streaks alternating with purplish under-leaf shadows. And the dark, curved horn projecting from its tail tapers off into space, distracting the eye from the caterpillar's

* Or do the next best thing and view it through green glass.

hinder end, which is not so slender as the stalk that joins leaf to stem. A pale line down the caterpillar's back suggests a midrib and completes the illusion.

CAMOUFLAGE FOR AGGRESSION

We will now consider a few predatory or carnivorous animals whose camouflage assists them in the capture of their prey.

First, the tiger, with its black stripes on a coat of tawny orange, and pale underparts. Its haunts are among tall grasses which for most of the year are dry and bleached to a yellowish colour, or among the reeds of swamps. The fierce light striking on the tall grass or reed-stems casts vivid black stripes of colour. In such a setting it is impossible to see a crouching tiger. Only the sudden rush of attack or lightning-like spring reveals its presence.

Various predatory fishes have interesting ways of approaching their prey. The garpike looks just like a log of wood; its eyes—the only feature that might betray it—are camouflaged by a dark stripe of colour that runs across them and continues the whole length of the head. The pike allows itself to drift with the stream until level with its prey, then, with a sudden sideways jerk of its head, it makes a capture. Both pike and perch, which live amongst reeds and rushes, are marked with stripes of darker colour.

The John Dory is a strange, mournful-looking fish often to be seen in an aquarium. Its body is compressed from side to side so as to be almost leaf-shaped, and has a large black spot on either flank. There is a legend that St. Peter once picked a John Dory out of the water with his finger and thumb, and that these fishes have borne the mark ever since. The John Dory keeps its body rigid and propels itself along by rapid undulations of transparent fins near the tail. In front view it is so thin as to appear like a mere streak or shadow in the water. When hunting it erects a back fin which increases its apparent height. The John Dory stalks small fish. Watching them closely, it draws nearer and nearer until, when within a few inches, its immense mouth opens, its protrusible jaws shoot forward, and the small fish is drawn in with the rush of water.

At least two foreign kinds of toads crouch motionless on the forest floor during the daytime, perfectly resembling the dead leaves scattered there. The toad waits for prey such as an insect to come within reach, then makes a lightning-quick dab with its sticky tongue. This flicks out, then in again, with the insect attached. One such toad (Plate 3) found in S. Africa resembles a leaf, both in shape and colour. Its body is flattened, and so is the top of its head. This flat surface is extended outwards by a ledge of skin along the flanks, a ledge which joins the ridge above the toad's eye. Of just the size and shape of a leaf, this flat surface is identical in colouring with the grey-brown, weather-stained leaves of the forest floor. From the skin ledge downwards, the toad's body is of rich chestnut-brown colour. This colour, being complementary to the greenish light coming through the leaves, gives an optical effect of black, and the black is enhanced by the real shadow cast by the ledge of skin. The resulting effect is a clear-cut deep shadow. So, as the result both of structure and of colour, the solid toad appears as an old discoloured leaf casting its shadow below. It escapes attack, and gives no warning of its presence to the small creatures it needs for food.

CHAPTER II

LIGHT, COLOUR AND VISION

To see and to be seen are possible only in the presence of light. For animals, this means the light of sun, moon, and stars.

In this matter of seeing, we must first clearly distinguish between three things that our human eyes report to us: brightness or intensity of illumination—strong light, dim light, or darkness; shape and other characteristics of objects around us; colours of objects. How much of all this do animals see? How much is in the eye of the beholder?

To be aware of light, of its strength or intensity, is of vital importance in the animal world. Apart from the obvious contrast between day and night, there are constant slight changes during the hours of darkness and of daylight—changes due to weather, passing clouds, the phases of the moon. At each hour between sunrise and sunset the height of the sun and the quality of the light differ, apart from the greater or lesser degree of light in summer and winter. All these light differences matter in the animal world.

The sun is the visible source of the life of nature, which it sustains. Living matter (protoplasm) is sensitive to light, responsive to it. The tiniest creatures, such as bacteria and *Amoeba*, mere specks of living matter, move into light of the strength best suited to their nature. Larger animals with organised bodies still show this sensitiveness to light, in that various parts of their skin are light-sensitive. The maggots of the blow-fly (the " gentles " of he bait shop), and the maggots that appear in cheese, show this very clearly. If we put some of these pale, eyeless maggots on a sheet of white paper in a dark room and shine a hand-torch along he paper, they move quickly and decidedly away from the source of light, for darkness is their safety and natural condition.

Although an earthworm has no eyes, it too is sensitive to light all over its skin, particularly at the head and tail ends.* Darkness or very dim light is natural to it, and it spends the hours of daylight n the ground. But in its burrowings to and fro the earthworm may thrust its head or tail end nearly out into the light—which means danger from the sharp eyes of birds. Its skin-sense generally warns the worm in time. At night, when there are fewer enemies about, worms often leave their burrows in search of food, or lie along the ground with just their tail-tips moored in their retreat. In the dim light of dawn they seem to enjoy an airing, with their heads stretched out of their holes. Hence the early bird catches the worm. Should we wish to test an earthworm's light-sense for ourselves, we have only to go out quietly just after dark, to a patch of short, damp turf. Here we shall find the worms half in and half out of their holes. Shine a hand torch on one. After a brief count—for a worm is not very " quick in the uptake "—the head disappears below: it vanishes within a second of sensing the light on its skin.

In many animals the skin as a whole is not light-sensitive, but certain spots are strongly so. Such " eye-spots " cause the animal to avoid too bright or too dim a light, and are really the beginnings of eyes. Snails and scallops, jellyfish and starfish are among the many animals with eye-spots. It is interesting that the pigment in many eye-spots is orange-red carotin, which is closely related in its chemical structure to the visual purple which plays so important a part in the eyes of Vertebrates.

In whatever other ways eyes may develop in the higher animals, they always retain this first important function of measuring the brightness or intensity of the light falling on them. Next, in creatures of a higher stage, comes the power to see the world outside themselves. It may be in a dim, vague way, as with the caterpillar, that can probably just make out a leaf up to two or three inches away from itself. Or it may be the keen, long-distance vision of man and bird. Every group of animals has its own pattern of eyes, just as it has its own shape and way of life. The less like ourselves the animal is, the less can we appreciate how it sees the

* In the skin are cells with a structure like a tiny lens which concentrates light on to nerve endings.

world.   To a great extent each kind of animal must live in a visual world of its own.

SIGHT

The seeing of objects and surroundings involves a special use of light—the light reflected from these objects into the eyes. Before there can be sight, there must be eyes, light, and a living being with a nervous system, a consciousness. Light, colour, and the appearance of things as we know them, for instance, exist only in our own mind : they accompany some special action of the brain.

So far as we can tell, there are very many animals that do not see colours. They see everything in black, white, and shades of grey, as in a photograph. A photograph can show a great deal ; in fact, it is easy to forget that a good photograph is not the real thing. At the cinema we are used to seeing everything in this way, and the sense of reality is not destroyed. Again, after wearing smoked or coloured glasses for a short time our eyes distinguish through them quite enough for all practical purposes. Most of the four-footed, warm-blooded animals (mammals) are thought to see their world in this " photographic " way. Careful observations on cats and dogs, for example, fail to show that they can distinguish a colour from a tone of grey of the same brightness. There are, too, slight differences of structure between their eyes and our own.

Most wild mammals feed or hunt at dusk and dawn or during the night. Both cats and mice are about at this time. Wild deer rest in cover during the day and feed in the twilight hours. During these hours there are no colours,* and the world is a study of glimmering white, grey, and black shadows. In their less active life of the daytime these wild creatures can see quite clearly without having a colour sense. Mammals are themselves clad in black, white, grey, or brown, their brightest colours being the chestnut or orange-browns of red squirrel, stoat, and giraffe. Only among apes and monkeys are bright colours such as red, green, and blue to be seen, and these animals, alone among mammals, have a colour sense.

ANIMALS MOVE ABOUT AT TIMES WHEN THEY CAN BEST SEE

The natural outdoor life of human beings belongs to the daylight hours. Rising with the sun and sleeping after sunset is the age-long practice of the peasant. The human eye works best in daylight. It adjusts itself to twilight, and by training can see to some

* Or perhaps one should say that the light is too dim for a colour analysing mechanism, such as an eye, to work.

extent even on a dark night; but this is using the instrument in a way for which it was never designed, and secures very poor results.

Everywhere a close connection is found between the kind of sight an animal has and the time of day or night when it moves about, plays, seeks its food, or finds a mate. Most birds go about their business in the daytime, when they can see, and are safe in their sleeping quarters before darkness sets in. Homing pigeons cannot continue on their way at night. Bees and wasps, butterflies, ladybirds, dragonflies, and a host of other familiar insects are busy in the daylight, weather permitting. Much is known about the eyes of bees and butterflies. They can see clearly only in a fairly good light. Especially is this true of butterflies. On a warm, bright summer day they are on the wing, or resting and feeding on the flowers. If a cloud passes over the sun they seem to disappear as if by magic—they have settled, or closed their wings, for they can no longer safely see their way about or detect an approaching enemy.

The night side of nature, hidden or motionless during the daylight hours, awakens as the light fades. At dusk bats flutter in the sky, hawking in search of insect food. Now they can see clearly—they are dazzled if disturbed in the daytime—and they hunt by starlight and moonlight, but not when the sky is pitchy black. Owls do the same: if they begin to hoot during a cloudy night it means that the sky has cleared enough for them to go hunting, or that dawn is near.

There is no doubt that some animals can use as "light" the infra-red rays, which to us are invisible. This is true of the prawns of the rock pools. Owls are able to catch mice in the dark because these very warm-blooded rodents emit infra-red rays which make them visible to the eyes of nocturnal birds. A patch of short grass on a dark night presents an astonishing stir of life during the warmer months of the year. Earthworms, leather-jackets, beetles, slugs, and snails are busy travelling and feeding. Perhaps a frog or a hedgehog goes by. Snails climb the bushes to feed on fruit and leaves, and the strange "stick" caterpillars that spend the daytime in rigid, trance-like stillness relax and feed on the leaves. Eyes, eye-spots, or sensitive skin—whichever these animals' outfit—all are attuned to the dim nocturnal light.

In desert regions it is seldom really dark, owing to the absence of night clouds. In the clear starlight near objects can be seen even by the human eye, and far more by the jackals, foxes, cats, and rodents that shelter during the burning heat of the day and emerge into the cool night world.

NIGHT-VISION OF OWLS AND CATS

" Pale one that comest in the night,
  The owl, the cat, the bat in thee delight."
                                    (Old spell.)

How often is the owl or cat used as a symbol of night ! The
eyes of these night hunters have much in common. In the dark a
cat's eyes look like two great black orbs. The pupil, like the shutter
of a camera used in poor light, is open to its widest extent, and we
look through this opening and through the lens into the black
space behind. The large eyes and widely opened pupils allow a
maximum of what light there is to fall on the sensitive region at
the back of the eye. The eyes are set on the front of the head and
look forwards—an unusual condition in birds and beasts, whose
eyes for the most part look sideways, each forming its own image.
In the cat and owl each eye forms an image of the same object from
a slightly different angle, so that the conscious impression is doubled
and made more intense. Hence also the appreciation of the distance
of the object. The retina of the eye, the light-sensitive part which
answers to the film or plate of the camera, has unusual numbers of
sense-cells suited to twilight vision. These cannot stand the bright
light of day, and are shielded by the almost complete closing of the
pupil-shutter of the eye. In daylight all we see is a black slit where
light enters. The owl has an extra advantage; the pupil-shutter
adjusts itself instantly to a change of light; it does not take several
seconds to accommodate, as does our own.

Domestic cats, of course, see quite well in the daytime and partly
adjust their time-table to their owner's habits, but most kinds of
owls can hardly see at all in daylight and remain hidden for safety.
However, the Little Owl can be heard and seen in daylight, and it
is not unusual to catch a glimpse of a big pale Barn Owl coasting
silently across a meadow.

COLOUR VISION

During the day, waves or rays of varied length stream from the
sun to the earth. One group of these waves we call light. Sometimes they are caught and reflected by the water-drops of clouds
in such a way that we see a rainbow—the familiar seven colours of
the spectrum. The longest of the " light " wave-lengths appear
red to the human eye, the shortest appear violet.

Solar radiation contains waves of many other lengths besides
those that appear as white light or as the colours of the spectrum.
Longer waves, known as infra-red, merge into still longer heat
waves. Waves shorter than violet, known as ultra-violet, merge

into still more rapid and powerful types. The human eye may be thought of as a receiving set for solar electric rays between the wave-lengths of about 4000 Å (red) and 8000 Å (violet), just as a wireless set is an instrument for receiving wave-lengths between about 300 and 700 metres. The middle of the violet region of the spectrum is of the wave-length of 4200 Å, while the middle of the red is of about 7000 Å.*

But when we think of colour, it is coloured objects, not coloured light, that come to our mind's eye. Daylight, the source of colour, seems almost invisible, certainly colourless. It is coloured clouds that make the sunset. The blue of the sky and the green of the grass, the colours of our clothes and furniture, all are caused by the complex white light striking objects and being split up and reflected from them in special ways, or passing through them as in coloured glass. A leaf appears green because it is full of a material that absorbs all light-rays except the green and yellow ones, which it reflects. A tomato is red because it contains material which reflects certain red wave-lengths, absorbing all others. Thus, as a green tomato ripens, its chemistry changes, and from having absorbed everything except green, it now absorbs all but certain reds.

Materials that absorb some waves and reflect others are, for convenience, called pigments. Pigments that absorb *all* the wave-lengths appear black, and those that absorb none, but reflect the whole spectrum, appear white. Some colours are not due to pigments, but are the result of light striking materials of special texture. Pigment colours and texture colours form the topic of Chapter III.

Yet though we now know how colours result from the action of light on material objects, there remains the old question : Is there really such a thing as red, or is "red" merely a sensation within ourselves? The reality of red or of any other colour cannot be proved by reasoning. All we know for certain is that suitable eyes, and consciousness working through a nervous system, give the experience of colour; and that a slight difference in make-up results in a completely colour-blind person, or in animals not greatly different in their structure from man, yet without a colour sense.

ANIMALS WHOSE COLOUR-SENSE DIFFERS FROM OUR OWN

Owls, as we have seen, make special use of the deep red waves, and it is probable that they use part of the infra-red waves as well.

* Å. = Ångstrom unit, which is one ten-millionth of a mm. See Appendix I.

Some scientists have lately questioned their use of infra-red, as a result of laboratory experiments. But since it is well known that the green pigment of plants reflects a good deal of infra-red light, it is quite possible that an owl flying over a meadow could really see a pale glimmer on the grass, when it would fail to see the much smaller expanse of infra-red possible in an indoor experiment. If it is difficult to imagine any animal "seeing" by means of infra-red rays, we have only to remember photographs taken with an infra-red-sensitive film. Thus on one occasion the authors took a colour photo of a misty landscape near the sea, using a Dufay colour film. The subsequent positive showed a clear-cut edge to the horizon, hilltops, etc., showing that the film was sensitive to infra-red, and that infra-red penetrates mist better than do other rays. It is now known, too, that the night-sky is full of a special light, a permanent aurora, due to the green of oxygen gas.

The owl's eyes are also specially sensitive to the violet end of the spectrum. This seems strange at first, but, as photographers know, there is more violet light in the spectrum in the early hours of the morning (e.g., 5 a.m. to 7 a.m. in March) than at any other time in the twenty-four hours. These hours are much used by owls for hunting.

The bees, so much in their element on a bright sunny day, make little use of the lower end of the spectrum, but full use of the blue and violet waves. They see the ultra-violet waves as well—waves which to our eyes are merely darkness.

Much attention has been given to the colour sense of bees. Their importance in pollinating flowers and in gathering nectar to convert into honey, has naturally led to much study of their habits. The visits of bees to flowers suggest that they see colours, and a list of the flowers they visit most often is found to include many of blue and purple colour. However, some flowers attract bees not by their colour, but by scent, by pollen, or by a profusion of faintly perfumed nectar. Holly, ivy, lime, and willow flowers are cases in point. Bees do not see red as a colour; they cannot tell red from dark grey or black. But this does not prevent them from visiting certain flowers of pure red, such as the scarlet runner. Many flowers that seem pink or red to our eyes must appear blue to the bees, for they are not pure red—they have a blue component. We can see this by looking at such flowers as foxglove or pink stock through green glass, which cuts out the red wave-lengths and allows only the blue to be seen. So when you see bees visiting red or pink flowers, they may be seeing them as blue. But such flowers are rarely bee-favourites.

The bee's special colour sense must make its world look different from our own in another interesting way. "White" surfaces by no means always look white to them—it depends on whether the surface reflects or absorbs the ultra-violet waves. White surfaces which absorb these rays appear blue-green to the bee and attract it. Thus many flowers with white or pale-tinted petals appear more colourful to bees than they do to us. The bees of Europe may be said to live in a world of orange-yellow, blue-green, and blue-violet.

Many experiments have been made to investigate the colour sense of bees; some will be found in *The Personality of Animals*.* Here is a somewhat rough-and-ready experiment planned and carried out by the authors, and which the reader can repeat. We made a number of simple flowers the shape of a wild rose, cut out of thin cardboard. Through the centre of each we put a twist of cellophane opened out to form a tiny cup. Each flower was fastened to a pointed stick. Two flowers were painted bright yellow, one blue, and three were lightly tinted with grey. The grey was the same tone or shade as the yellow, tested by looking at both through grey sun glasses (not "Crookes" glass). This was to make sure that grey and yellow were of just the same tone; in other words, had we been colour-blind we could not have distinguished yellow from grey.

Next we put diluted honey in the cellophane cup of a yellow flower and stuck it in the lawn, facing the sun. The day was warm and sunny. Before long bees discovered the honey and returned repeatedly to the flower after taking a load of honey to the hive. Then we removed the honey-filled yellow flower and put an empty blue and an empty yellow near by. The bees ignored the blue and went to the yellow flower, showing that they connected the yellow colour with honey. To find whether the bees really saw yellow, or merely a certain tone of grey, we next stuck yellow and grey flowers, all honey-filled, in a cluster together. The great majority of the bees still chose the yellow.

On another day we trained the bees to come to a honey-filled red flower, and then found they could not distinguish red from a group of black and dark grey flowers. When all contained honey, the bees visited them equally. During these experiments the bees made movements that seemed to indicate awareness that the flowers were not normal; they showed slight unrest.

It has been found that bees can see in ultra-violet light by throwing a wide spectrum (using a powerful light shining through a prism)

* See Bibliography.

on to a white table in a dark room. The bees can be trained to go for syrup to the ultra-violet region of light. Other animals that react to ultra-violet light are the water fleas, *Daphnia*, and Planarians.

Butterflies are also known to have colour vision. The peacock butterfly, for instance, has about the same colour range as the bee. On the whole, butterflies prefer red and white colours.

The Colour Sense of Birds

It would be strange indeed if birds, whose plumage can display some of the most brilliant colours in the world, should lack a colour sense. We take it for granted that rosy, scarlet, crimson and purple fruits attract birds on account of their colour, and that the bright colours of cock birds can be seen by their mates. Yet is it a mere assumption? Is there any proof that birds see colours?

Experiment shows that birds see red, orange, yellow and green colours clearly, but that they do not see blue very well and do not see violet at all. To test the colour sense of the domestic hen a strong lamp was set up in a dark room so as to shine through a prism,* and cast a spectrum, like the rainbow colours, on the floor. An equal number of grains was scattered in each band of coloured light. Then a hen was let into the room. She pecked up nearly all the grains that looked red, orange, yellow and green, but took very few of the grains in the blue light and none from the violet light. From these and other experiments it appears that birds can see the warm colours of ripe fruits and are attracted by them.

In some parts of the world many of the flowers are pollinated, not by insects, but by tiny humming-birds which poise for a second in front of a flower to dip their beaks into the flower tube for nectar. From travels in Brazil, South Africa and West Australia, Werth lists 159 flowers visited by birds, and 84% of these are red. Red is highly attractive to the humming-birds of all countries, and nearly all the flowers they visit for nectar are red, orange or purple (red with blue). It is interesting to compare with this the " Hermit Hummers " of Brazil, which " . . . are all very plainly coloured birds with little metallic colouring, sometimes none, and instead of living in the sunshine and feeding among flowers, they inhabit the gloomy forests and subsist wholly on insects gleaned from the branches and leaves of trees." †

In the colouring of birds themselves, violet is not found, and blue is not common. But when a bird *has* blue feathers they are

* A triangular glass rod. † Thompson.

a definite and bright blue, as in the macaw, kingfisher, jay and blue tit. This fits in with the probability that birds do not see blue very clearly, and it must be really bright if they are to see it as a colour. It is interesting to notice that there are practically no blue foods for either birds or mammals.

THE COLOUR-SENSE OF FISHES AND SHRIMPS

There are fishes that can see colours quite well. The shanny (*Blennius pholis*), one of our shore fishes, can distinguish clearly between a wide range of colours, and the minnow (*Phoxinus*) does the same. If these fish are offered food lit by a beam of coloured light or placed in a tube lined with coloured paper, they soon learn to connect food with a definite colour such as yellow. Then if a yellow object is placed in their tank they make straight for it, expecting something to eat. They can distinguish between yellow and a shade of grey of the same brightness.

Some kinds of fish strongly suggest that they see colours, since they adjust their own skin colours according to the colour of the background on which they find themselves. The same is true of the shrimps and prawns of our coasts. The subject of colour change in such animals is dealt with later.

THE MACHINERY FOR COLOUR VISION

In this review of some of the animals so far known to have a colour sense we find that this faculty is not confined to one pattern of eye. Fishes and birds have eyes very similar to our own, but the eyes of bees, butterflies and prawns are quite differently made. Can we point to any part of the eye and say, " This is the part that has to do with seeing colour "? In the human eye and others like it, the answer is probably " Yes ". The sensitive lining of the eye, the retina, answers to the film or plate of a camera. In the retina are great numbers of sense-cells of two distinct kinds; these are called rods and cones because of the shape of their ends. The rods and cones respond to the intensity of light falling on them; they send different messages to the nerves of the eye with every different grade of light that reaches them. The rods register dim, and the cones bright, intensities of light.

It is known that the rods need vitamin A to keep them sensitive to very dim light. This vitamin is present in foods such as cod-liver oil and other animal fats, and to a lesser extent in eggs. But animals and man can readily convert carotin into vitamin A in their own bodies, so that carotin in food is almost as valuable as vitamin A itself. Carotin is easily obtained in the form of green vegetables, carrot and tomato. In the rods is a special pigment concerned with twilight vision and called visual purple. Visual purple is bleached by bright light into vitamin A and another chemical. When we pass suddenly from a bright to a dim light, we cannot at first see at all. Then in a few seconds the visual purple is re-formed. Now it can respond to the dim light, and we feel our eyes adjusted to this. So this adjustment of the eyes to dim light is a matter of chemistry; lack of vitamin A prevents the rebuilding of visual purple which normally takes place in darkness when there is a sufficiency of the vitamin.

During accommodation to a recently changed light intensity the pupil contracts or dilates to regulate the amount of light reaching the retina.

Probably the cones alone respond to the separate wave-lengths which become interpreted as colour.* The cones are specially numerous at one particular spot (the yellow spot) in the retina of each eye. When we turn our eyes to look at an object, we turn them until these two spots are exactly in line with the object, at which moment we see it most clearly. The distinction between the uses of rods and cones is not clear in the lowest verte-brate animals. For instance, in different kinds of bony fishes the retina may contain both rods and cones, or rods or cones alone. And the visual purple, which varies in light-absorption capacities, is not confined to the rods.

It is not yet known whether any one part of the insect eye is specially concerned with colour vision.

Whether we discover the exact machinery of colour vision or not, the fact remains that the eyes of different animals interpret the same group of solar rays in different ways. And in man there are three kinds of colour-blindness in addition to "normal" colour vision. Man, bird and beast interpret as light and colour slightly different groups of these solar rays. All see the world in their own way—perhaps none see it as it really is. None the less, the solar rays act upon the animals whether they are seen as colours, as photographic tones, or not "seen" at all. We have only to remember the powerful effects of ultra-violet rays on the human subject—rays that are invisible to his eyes.

Experiments you Can Make

(1) At night, take a lighted candle, stand at the entrance to a dark room or passage, and wave the candle about gently before your eyes, looking past the flame into the darkness. Soon you will see

* See Chap. XI.

an appearance like leafless branches—the blood vessels of the retina, part of which is reflected out through the lens on to the screen of the darkness.

(2) Watch in a mirror, and time, the contraction and dilation of the pupils of your eyes. Sit for five minutes in a dark room with eyes closed. Then look in the mirror, with a lighted candle or electric torch held close to the eyes. When the pupils have fully contracted, note what time has elapsed. Then allow them to dilate again to varying extents in darkness, getting a rough estimate of time by counting slowly one hundred, two hundred and so on.

CHAPTER III

NATURE'S PIGMENTS AND COLOUR EFFECTS

Most plants and animals show colour as a natural part of their structure. Ordinary plants are green, with coloured flowers, and fungi are coloured, or black or white. Among animals the same is true, though in the sea there are transparent creatures with hardly a trace of colour. The most colourless animals we are ever likely to see are the jellyfish, but even they have spots or crescents or lines of colour.

The living material or protoplasm of which plants and animals are built is not coloured. Under a microscope it appears like glass filled with minute specks and bubbles, and tiny clear pools. But life means activity, and protoplasm is constantly at work: one of the things it does is to manufacture materials for various purposes—materials which may be coloured or colourless. Saliva, for instance, is colourless, while liver bile is yellow or green. Any material that colours the inside or outside of an animal is called a "pigment"; the name, taken from its use in the arts, thus includes black and white, as well as brighter colours.

WHERE PIGMENTS COME FROM

Since plants are the source of food for animals * it is natural to enquire first whether animals make their own pigments or derive them from those of plants.

The most important plant pigment is leaf-green, chlorophyll,†

---

* Vegetarian animals feed directly on plants, and carnivorous animals eat flesh which has been built up directly or indirectly from plant food.

† From the Greek, *chloros*, green, and *phyllon*, leaf.

important because the plant's carbohydrate foods are built up by chlorophyll with the aid of solar energy. In a sense, plants live by light. Chlorophyll is a mixture of green, blue-green and yellow pigments, a fact that helps to account for the great variety of green tints to be seen in any garden or countryside, and for the yellow tint of young oak leaves in spring before the green pigments in them have increased.

Land animals that feed on grass and leaves eat plenty of chlorophyll. Marine animals that feed on seaweed do the same, for whatever their apparent colour, all seaweeds contain chlorophyll. In spite of this, animal greens are rarely due to chlorophyll. It colours the liver of various snails and shellfish; the famous " green oysters " of Marennes owe their colour to the minute sea plants on which they feed. Various green caterpillars have a form of chlorophyll in solution in the blood, and this gives their skin a green tint. The caterpillar of the Angle Shades Moth is green because the food in its digestive system shows through its transparent body. The yolks of duck eggs sometimes have a greenish tint which some farmers put down to the food they eat, but which may in some cases be a hereditary factor. These, however, are all examples of green colour *inside* the animal. Green pigments in the skin itself are almost entirely animal products; for instance the green of the marine ragworm *Eulalia*, and of greenfly and many green caterpillars. The brightest greens, such as those of lizards and frogs, and the feathers of birds, are not due to green pigments at all. We shall see later how they come about.

We have said that chlorophyll is a mixture of green and yellow pigments. One of the yellow pigments, the well-known carotin (or carotene), gives their red, yellow, and orange colours to many fruits, flowers, and vegetables. Carrot, mangold, and tomato are familiar examples. The second yellow pigment is named xanthophyll. The carotin pigments animals obtain from their plant-food colour their internal parts in many ways. The yellow of egg-yolk, used as a pigment by many old masters in their paintings, is a carotin. The pink colour of the flesh of the salmon is due to a carotin pigment in the fat, the yellow colour of the oils extracted from cod and halibut liver has the same source, as also the yellow of butter and the elegant bright yellow " fat bodies " which are an internal supply of food in frogs, toads and their kin.

A curious instance of the effect of carotin food on the consumer was shown by a family who had to consult a doctor because their skins became yellow and they thought they had jaundice. For some time they had eaten an excessive amount of raw chopped carrot—quite 8 lb. a week—in addition to cooked carrot. The trouble was soon settled by leaving carrots out of their diet for a short time. One kind of yellow hair owes its colour to a carotin pigment, as does red hair. It should be noted that carotin has many slightly different forms in plants, and when within the animal body is usually altered to a greater or less extent before appearing as an animal pigment.

The second yellow pigment in green leaves, xanthophyll, may on occasion colour animal tissues. When a rabbit, for example, eats and digests green food, the xanthophyll pigment is broken down by an enzyme in the liver, the resulting material being colourless. Some strains of rabbits, however, are without this enzyme, and the xanthophyll passes into the fat, colouring it yellow. Most of us do not care to eat rabbits with yellow-coloured fat, so their market value is spoiled. If such rabbits are fed on a diet which excludes green food (white corn, mash, potatoes), their fat can be kept white. The yellow of the wings of certain butterflies, *Papilio* and other groups, is due to still another plant yellow (anthoxanthin), eaten by the caterpillars as they feed on plants.

We may say, then, that the plant pigments eaten by animals tend to colour some of their internal parts, but more rarely give their skin colours. And while plants are marked out by their green colour, green is not a characteristic colour of animals. We will explore further into the source of animal pigments.

OTHER KINDS OF ANIMAL PIGMENTS

In the great diversity of animals without backbones—the Invertebrate group (sea anemones, starfish, worms, shellfish, crabs, and so on), skin pigments are of many different kinds. Often they differ from one animal to another, and can be arranged only roughly in chemical groups. In the backboned Vertebrate group, however, pigments are not so diverse. All Vertebrates have red blood, and blood is the starting-point from which a variety of pigments proceed. The scarlet pigment that colours the blood-cells is known as hæmoglobin. It is this that produces the red lips and pink cheeks in man. Blood-cells have a life of only three weeks or so, after which they are broken down mainly in the spleen, new ones constantly taking their place. In the liver, useful parts of the complex hæmoglobin pigment are removed for use again, and other parts got rid of in various ways. The bile made by the liver contains a green and a red pigment, both of which are break-down products of hæmoglobin. The beautiful blues, greens, and reds of birds' eggs are nearly all from this source. Some birds' eggs have a yellow tint, which is due to still another pigment resulting from hæmoglobin, as is the brown of hens' eggs.

Before leaving the subject of hæmoglobin we may see how closely it resembles chlorophyll. Both hæmoglobin and chlorophyll are very complex chemical materials built on the same peculiar pattern around what we may term a similar "kernel". But the key element of the chlorophyll kernel is magnesium, to which the element iron corresponds in the hæmoglobin kernel. Chlorophyll pigment is essential to the life of green plants, and hæmoglobin to that of vertebrates, the most successful group of animals. It is tempting to enquire whether chlorophyll is particularly useful as a food from which animal protoplasm can build up hæmoglobin, and there is some ground for the belief that this is the case.

Black, brown, and certain tawny-yellow colours are due to a pigment called melanin. Melanin is formed in the living tissues from a material which commonly and normally results from the digestion of protein foods. The coloured pigment is formed from its colourless "precursor" * if a certain enzyme is present, and the process can, as a rule, take place only in the presence of light.† Thus internal chemistry determines external pigmentation. Black and brown hair and eyes in man and animals, tanned and olive skins, the black, brown, and some of the yellow colours of skin and scales in lizards, snakes, frogs, fish, all are due to melanin. Melanin is quite common in Invertebrate animals also.

Melanin is nearly always present in the eye, whatever its exact structure in different animals. The melanin acts as an opaque screen which prevents light from passing beyond the eye into the body. In some positions melanin can give the effect of blue colour. Blue eyes in man are due to melanin at the *back* of the iris. This is the pigment present in the eyes of young babies, and the blue is often gradually hidden by the formation of melanin *in front* of the iris, making the eye appear brown. Blue eyes are sometimes erroneously explained as due to total absence of pigment.

The particles of melanin at the back of the iris are so small that they are in a colloidal state. They are too small to reflect light-waves, but scatter them instead. The wave-lengths scattered with maximum intensity are the shortest ones, the blue, so that it is those that we notice. The same effect is seen in the case of blue smoke or mist. The melanin formed in front of the iris is pre-

* Precursor, the amino acid tyrosine: enzyme, tyrosinase.
† Except for the black pigment lining the body cavity of some Amphibia.

sumably distributed in larger particles, or else in sufficient quantity to allow of so much absorption that scattering is relatively unimportant.*

During its complex functioning, the animal body gives rise to a number of chemical materials which are waste products, and would be harmful if retained. In some animals these can be got rid of conveniently in the usual ways, but in others they may be deposited in the skin in a harmless form and assist in the colouring of the body. A well-known example is the white and yellow of the wings of certain Pierid butterflies—for example, the Swallow-tail. This pigment is allied to uric acid. The beautiful mirror-like sides of a fish are due to guanin pigment, of which another form is the white pigment (in Iridocytes) in the skin of frogs and toads. These latter pigments are of the nature of waste products.

In the light of their origin, then, we may describe many animal pigments as the products of various activities of the body. Some result from the direct absorption or digestion of food—for example the carotin pigments in hair, derived from plant food, and the melanin which is formed from a product of protein digestion. Other pigments are produced by the activity of an organ such as the spleen, and passed to the liver, which excretes them as bile pigments, the result of breakdown of red blood corpuscles.

Pigments for Light Sensitivity

Once such pigments exist, they may prove very useful in the animal economy. Let us turn back to the minute creatures, Protozoa, whose bodies are of colourless protoplasm. In the amoeba, for instance, the protoplasm must allow all wave-lengths to penetrate equally: although able to tell bright from dim light, the amoeba can be light-sensitive only in a general way. But where the chemistry of the minute animal or plant gives rise to a spot of red pigment, the power of selection is now possible. The red " eye-spot " allows for perception of green light and green things, and this may be important in getting food. There is now selective light response: the environment, in however small a way, begins to be organised. For analogy we may remember how to the eyes of a newly born baby the environment is just a blur, but as more pigment develops in the eyes, coloured objects can be distinguished. Red eye-spots are found in a number of aquatic

* It has also been suggested that the apparent blue may be the complementary colour to melanin (which can have a reddish tint), and this would explain the optical effect.

dwellers; the Rotifers or Wheel animalcules, several swimming forms of one-celled plants, such as *Euglena* and *Chlamydomonas*, in larval marine worms (Polychaeta) and Echinoderms, and even in large creatures, such as the starfish, though here the eye-spot is more than a mere speck of pigment. Red eye-spots mostly contain carotin. As we have already seen, carotin is a precursor of vitamin A, which is closely related to the light-sensitive visual purple. Melanin is also found in eye-spots, as in flatworms, medusae, and small Crustacea.

Again, light spread evenly over a surface has different effects from light focused at a point, as the use of a burning-glass clearly shows. Light focused in a pigment spot means the definite absorption of more energy at that spot. Once the light-sensitive pigment spot exists, we have the potential for the development of the eye. Every pattern of eye depends partly on pigment for its correct working. The sensitive response of various pigments and pigment cells to light is also shown by their movements during the accommodation of the eyes of various animals to different light intensities, a subject to which we return in Chapter XI. It is also shown by the direct response to light of the pigment cells of most animals which change their colour.

PROTECTION FROM EXCESS LIGHT

Pigments on the surface of an animal may be very useful as a protection from too much light. Although light is beneficial, it can also be dangerous, if not fatal, to delicate tissues. Screens of pigment are found in various colourless animals, allowing them to be exposed to light which might otherwise be harmful. We find, for instance, that the prawn, with its transparent skin and glassy muscles, has a network of pigment over the nerves that pass up its eye-stalks, and that in bright light there is a slight spreading of colour in the pigment cells over all the exposed parts of the body. The common sea anemone found on the rocks of the sea-shore when the tide is down, and looking like a lump of red or brown jelly, is able to withstand exposure to brilliant light and hot sun partly on account of its heavy pigmentation. We recall the dense screen of melanin pigment in the skin and hair of peoples native to the tropics, protecting them from the otherwise deadly effect of the solar rays. Again, there is the protective bronzing of the skin of people of temperate zones if gradually exposed to bright sunlight, and the dangerous effect of too sudden or too long exposure to it. Bronzing by the sun is due to the formation of melanin in the skin.

ABSORPTION OF WARMTH

The uses of dark pigments, of course, depend on time and place. Under cold conditions black pigment which absorbs all light-waves may serve as a source of warmth, the red end of the spectrum being the most useful in this respect. The black cap of pigment on frog spawn is a case in point. Every bit of warmth in the March sun-shine, as it falls on the spawn floating on the surface of the pond, is absorbed by the black pigment. It is also noticeable that many small alpine creatures are black. In contrast, large warm-blooded birds and mammals are mostly white and match the snow.

So the surface colours of animals may serve a variety of uses—they may be light-sensitive, or protective, or heat-absorbing: they may take the form of a deposit of waste products, conveniently located in the skin. From such pigments, and such contributory causes, come the materials for the colour schemes and patterns which emerge as a finished response of animals to their environment.

RESPIRATORY PIGMENTS

A further immense advantage that accompanies the production of pigment is this, that certain pigments have the property of combining with oxygen and releasing this oxygen again to the living cells that demand it. Oxygen is essential to life, and the uptake and use of oxygen must go on every moment. The more oxygen a creature can use, the brighter burns its flame of life and the greater are its possible activities.

Minute creatures of protoplasm, such as the amoeba, take in their oxygen all over their surface, direct from air or water. But when the body becomes larger, many cells no longer have access to oxygen in this way, and some means must be found of carrying oxygen to them. Some animals, such as sponges, sea squirts, and starfish, cause a slow stream of sea or fresh water to pass through their bodies, and from this, oxygen can be absorbed. A further advance, and one essential for land animals, is the development of a closed " circulatory system " no longer opening directly to the outside, but coming at certain points so close to the surface as to allow the contained fluid to absorb oxygen. Gills and lungs are instances of regions where the circulatory fluid comes very close to the oxygen-carrying air or water, being separated only by an ex-ceedingly thin skin. So far, so good; but by what means can more oxygen be drawn into the circulatory fluid? There are certain pigments—respiratory pigments, as they are called—which readily combine with, and release, oxygen. Hæmoglobin, with its iron basis, is the most efficient of all. Although hæmogolbin is the respiratory pigment of backboned animals alone, a similar iron-containing pigment has been produced independently in widely differing animal groups. There is a kind of fresh-water snail (*Planorbis*) that has red blood; it is found in " bloodworms ", which are the aquatic larvæ of a gnat, and in earthworms, lugworms, and the little *Tubifex* earthworms of fresh water.

Hæmoglobin provides a notable case of the intimate relationship between the physiology of any group of animals and the nature of their pigments. Each animal group has its own form of hæmoglobin; a specialist can recognise bird hæmoglobin from that of a fish, for example, on account of the shape of crystals that appear during analysis. Different kinds vary in their power of carrying oxygen. Bird hæmoglobin is the most efficient oxygen-carrier known, and this is one reason why birds are capable of the intense activity of flight. Hæmoglobin is red when carrying oxygen (in arteries), and blue or purple when carrying little or no oxygen (in veins). The difference in colour can be seen clearly in the blood vessels of the human wrist.

Another respiratory pigment, named hæmocyanin, with a basis of copper, occurs in the blood of the great shellfish group (Mollusca) and the lobster, insect, and spider group (Arthropoda). Hæmocyanin is pale blue when carrying oxygen, and colourless or straw-coloured when deprived of oxygen. It does not tint the surface or the flesh in the same way that hæmoglobin colours the lips, tongue, and muscles of Vertebrates. Copper must be present when hæmoglobin is formed, and iron present when hæmocyanin is being made. A small group of marine worms is distinguished by possessing green respiratory pigment in its blood. (A table of respiratory pigments is given in Appendix II.)

Thus pigments appear again not merely as colours, but as products which help to make possible such faculties as sight and intensified activity, quite apart from the manifold beauties and intricacies of external colour and pattern. Man, also, has found for various pigments uses unknown to nature. Such is the Tyrian purple, once so extensively used for dyeing, and obtained from various snails of the marine dog-whelk type, *Purpura* and *Murex*. A gland in these snails produces a secretion of grey-green colour whose function is so far unknown. When this secretion is exposed to light it turns a deep purple colour, and the dyeing was done in open vats in the presence of sea water.

COLOURS DUE TO SURFACE STRUCTURE

The colours we have so far described are due to definite material pigments. Such pigments can be extracted from the tissues containing them and studied by chemical analysis and spectroscopic methods. But various animal colours are due to the effects of light playing on surfaces which, unlike pigments, absorb no part of it. Such colours are termed optical or structural. These, of course, cannot be extracted.

The white in shrimps, frogs, and fishes is due to a white pigment, but the white of fur and of feathers is a structural colour. Innumerable tiny air bubbles are enmeshed in their substance; these reflect all light-waves and give the appearance of white. The white of foam is caused in the same way. The enclosed air is incidental—it is the curves and facets of the bubble surfaces that produce the effect, by the way they catch the light.

We are familiar with the rainbow colours caused by the play of light on the thin film of a soap bubble, or on an oil film on the damp surface of a road. Here we are seeing colours in the absence of pigments. Such colour effects can be seen on the surface of any thin transparent material—for example, a thin plate of mica. Mother of pearl is an example of structural colour. We see its pearly lustre and delicate play of colour in the lining of many shells. Sometimes it is to be seen on the outside of empty sea-shells whose outer coating has been worn away by constant tumbling on the shore; again, large shells are sometimes dipped in acid to remove the outer layer and expose the pearly layer for ornamental purposes. The pearly lustre is caused by the laying down of layer upon layer of the mineral calcite (calcium carbonate). The delicate colours result from the play of light on and through the tiny mineral crystals at the surface.

Some of the most brilliant colours in nature—the feathers of the peacock and humming-bird, and the scales of butterflies and beetles—are due to the play of light on special surfaces. Feathers have a thin covering of horny material. The scales of insects have a thin film of a material known as chitin, and such scales cover the wings of most butterflies and moths. This covering may be thin and flat or sculptured and ridged in manifold ways; it may be colourless or tinted. The surface film of horn or chitin thus presents great possibilities for optical effects. In some instances the same principle is found as that used in making " shot " silk. The brilliant, almost metallic lustre on the wings of the blue Morpho butterfly of South America, so extensively used for ornaments, is an instance of surface structure enhancing pigment colour from one angle, and giving its own optical green when seen from another angle. Green may be entirely an optical colour. In birds it may result from surface effect alone, or more usually from surface effect combined with yellow, grey, or brown pigment in the feathers. The Blue-fronted Amazon Parrot has green feathers which turn dull brown if the bird becomes thoroughly drenched. The wet surface loses its optical effects. Sometimes, no doubt, the natural oil with which the bird preens its feathers plays an important part. The brilliant green of some butterflies (e.g., *Ornithoptera poseidon*) is caused by structural blue overlying yellow pigment.

Many reptiles owe their brilliance or variety of colours to a combination of pigment and optical effect. Lizards such as the Iguanid (*Anolis*) and the chameleon have a skin with layers of different pigments under a covering of almost transparent horny material in the form of scales. The iguanid has branching pigment cells containing melanin in the base of its skin, then a layer of pigment cells containing yellow oil droplets, and over these a layer of pigment cells which have almost colourless contents, but give the optical effect of blue, on account of the way the contents scatter the light. The melanin can stream up branches which run among the yellow and blue layers, or spread over the top of them, or it can retreat until out of view at the bottom. Thus the skin can display yellowish, emerald-green, blue-green, and mahogany colours from the interplay of the two pigments and the colourless layer of leucophore pigment cells.

CHAPTER IV

CAMOUFLAGE IN THE SEA

OUR information regarding the deeper waters depends on the descriptions of a diver, of a scientist who dons a diving-helmet and descends to the sea-bottom in clear, shallow water, or of an artist who finds means of sketching under the water, and so records his direct impressions. All such explorers express in some way the fascination and distinctiveness of structure and light quality of under-water life. Robert Gibbings writes of his first impressions of a Bermuda reef, "It was like being in some great cathedral lit by pale-green glass."

A great deal can be seen and understood regarding the animal life of the shore and off-shore waters. We can watch the animals in a rock pool, or observe those at greater depths from the side of a boat. Many of Aristotle's far-reaching studies were made as he lay in a boat and looked into the clear, brilliantly lit sea around the Ægean Isles. There were probably early pioneers of submarine investigation. An old picture purports to illustrate the story that King Alfred had a kind of barrel made, in which he was lowered into the Thames.

A good aquarium can give a very fair imitation of sea animals and plants in their natural condition. But, even so, we are still *outside* the picture, not a part of it, and even if we were, human eyes see but poorly under water unless after long practice such as is gained by pearl and sponge-divers.

Of the physical conditions in sea water, that which specially concerns our subject is light. How does living in the sea affect the amount and quality of light, and hence the colours, patterns and camouflage of sea animals? Between tide-marks and on the sea bottom in shallow water exists a well-lighted and mostly colourful world where form, hue and resemblance to environment follow the general lines we are familiar with on land. It is in the medium of the upper waters that new effects are to be expected, as also in the deeper waters to which little or no light penetrates.

LIGHT IN THE SEA

The light in the sea depends on depth, time of day, season, and weather conditions. Light penetrates more deeply into clear water than into water made turbid by sand or mud.

Only on rare occasions can the whole of the sun's light penetrate the actual surface of the sea. When the sun is directly overhead and there is a dead calm, this can occur. For the most part the sea surface acts as a barrier to light-waves, reflecting them back to a greater or lesser extent, according to the angle at which the rays strike the surface. The reflection on the waves can often be quite dazzling to the eyes of an observer from above.

The light that enters the sea passes down and is slowly absorbed. The light conditions in the English Channel, off Plymouth, are, for instance, at ten fathoms (60 ft.), similar to those in the shadiest part of a beechwood in summer. At greater depths the light becomes more and more dim, until it fades altogether and complete darkness reigns. Not only the brightness but also the quality of the light alters in passing from the surface downwards. The red end of the spectrum is quickly absorbed near the surface, then the other wave-lengths in the order orange, yellow, green. Blue and violet light penetrate most deeply, and in clear sea—for instance in the Sargasso region of the Atlantic—violet light has been detected at 550 fathoms. (The blue colour of the sea is caused by the upward reflection of light waves striking small particles in the water. Both in descending and ascending through the water wave-lengths other than green, blue and violet are absorbed: only these can emerge again to give the sea its colour. Light reflected from the sea surface often alters the colour of the sea, as on a day of sun and cloud, or when the hues of sunrise and sunset are mirrored on the waves.)

Since light of some strength penetrates only to comparatively slight depths, the area of growth of plants on the sea bottom is strictly limited. On the sea-shore and down to 15 or 20 fathoms seaweeds grow wherever there are rocks or stones to which they can fix themselves, though the growth is richest down to the 10-fathom line. On the shore, between tide-marks, light is intense. Here brown is the commonest colour for the shore seaweeds: there is plenty of chlorophyll concealed in the brown weeds, and chlorophyll reflects light in the hot infra-red region of the spectrum. The brown itself apparently gives some protection against excess light. Red seaweeds appear near low-tide mark, and red is the most usual colour for those in deep water. This seems to be partly due to the fact that red weeds naturally absorb blue-green light-waves, and it is these that are available to them, and partly because the red weeds mostly thrive better in shady conditions and are unable to stand the brilliant light on the shore.

A great variety of animals make their home in the natural setting of rock and weeds, many using it for anchorage and protection, some feeding directly upon it. Crabs, starfish, sea-urchins, snails, anemones, sea-worms and a host of less familiar animals are found in this environment, and may in a general fashion be compared with the land fauna associated with land plants. With changes in the nature of the sea bottom, whether sand, gravel, rock or coral, and with its depth and other factors, occur changes in the fauna. Thus there is a geographical distribution of plants and animals on the sea bottom and between tide marks. And as on land there are insects and birds which rest, feed and shelter amongst the plants, but also launch themselves into the air as a means of travel, and sometimes as a hunting ground, so in the sea there are fish, cuttlefish, prawns and other animals which spend part of their time on the sea bottom and part in the water above. But whereas insects, birds and bats make no pretence of concealment while in flight, it is otherwise with many of the marine forms when moving in the water medium.

The realm of the sea has one important element in its population with which there is nothing to be compared on terra firma, namely a great swimming and floating population which spends its whole life in the upper waters, sinking to the sea bottom only when they die (Pelagic organisms). With them are others which pass the first weeks or months of their lives in this manner, but at a suitable age take to living on the shore or on the sea bottom. In this surface region, too, are the countless myriads of microscopic sea-weeds, the diatoms and desmids, fitly named the " pastures of the sea."

Small pelagic animals are almost all transparent, and are colour-less except for scattered pigment cells, or dark eye-spots, or a coloured patch caused by an organ such as liver or gonad. Al-though present in immense numbers, they are so inconspicuous that their presence in the water usually remains unsuspected.* The larger pelagic animals are opaque, but have characteristic colourings that blend them with their watery environment. They have a characteristic colour according to the depth and light con-ditions at which they occur. In the Sargasso Sea region, for instance, catches taken near the surface include blue flying fish and others of silvery aspect, small floating creatures of delicate blue or green and the transparent early stages of various fishes. At depths of 300 metres fish with brown backs and silvery sides are found, while fishes and prawns taken at depths below 500 metres are black or red. The colour schemes of these different depth populations (vertical distribution) confer a general incon-spicuousness on all and sundry, whether harmless and defenceless or predatory in habit. The colours mentioned are, of course, those seen in daylight after the fishes have been brought to the surface.

COUNTERSHADING IN THE WATER ENVIRONMENT

In the mid-water zone, moving freely up to the surface waters, are many well-known fishes. There are pelagic types, such as the mackerel and tunny, which are continuously on the move, and others, such as the hake, which leave the sea bottom during the night and swim freely in the upper waters. These, together with other familiar forms, such as herring, cod, shark, and dolphin, all show to the full the principle of counter-shading—dark back

* Under exceptional conditions plankton organisms can be so numerous as to tint the water over an area of miles. The protozoan *Noctiluca* may turn the water a pale tomato-soup colour; the copepod *Calanus*, so important as food for herring, makes the water red and is described as ' red feed " by fishermen. Various diatoms are responsible for red, yellow or green water.

grading to pale underside. In most, the counter-shading takes the form of a gradient from dark to pale in hues of grey, or grey with green and blue, but in mackerel and pilot fish a definite pattern adorns the all-over background of counter-shading.

This colour scheme affords a good degree of concealment whether its wearer is viewed from above, below, or from the side, as Cott clearly explains. If viewed from below, the white belly of the fish presents a silvery sheen whose iridescent surface displays a near approach to the bright surrounding background of sky or of surface film. From above, the dark back is difficult to recognise, being effaced against the colour of the ocean, which appears leaden or deep blue from above; this is the case with the brown-black back of the herring with its metallic lustre, and the same result is effected by the bright blue back of the flying fish against the blue of the tropical surface water. From the side, the insubstantial effect which always accompanies counter-shading (flat instead of three-dimensional) comes into play.

In deep sea zones such as those in some of the Norwegian fjords there are bright scarlet sea fans, red, yellow, and brown sea pens, and red and brown sea cucumbers. In the abyssal zone, where absolute darkness reigns, the creatures are black, red, grey, or deep brown. They are of uniform colour all over, with no pattern or markings of any kind. In such regions colour can be of no optical importance, and we expect no examples of camouflage.* The deep-sea fauna feeds on particles raining down from above, or on one another, sometimes aided by phosphorescent light produced by themselves, which is referred to later.

Camouflaged Animals of the Shore and Sea Floor

In the brightly-lit world of the shore and on the floor of the shallow sea the animals show much general resemblance in form and colour to their natural home, and some animals show a detailed likeness to special objects.

Collectors of sea-shore animals know that it needs a trained eye to detect many besides the conspicuous limpets, beadlet anemones, starfish, crabs, and winkles. A little flat pile of shingle and shell fragments, for instance, may be really a dahlia anemone with its tentacles tucked inside, and camouflaged with fragments of these materials stuck all over its body. The sea spiders (Pycnogonids)

---

* It has been suggested that the red pigmentation is the result of certain foods eaten by the deep sea creatures under conditions of very dim illumination, and that in better-lighted regions of the sea the resulting pigments would be yellow or white.

crouch under stones or among weeds with their long legs bunched together, looking just like a knot of fine seaweed. The beautiful translucent leaf-thin flatworms in shelter under boulders pass for a lobed patch of some encrusting coralline weed or sea-mat. Porcelane crabs appear as irregularities under the surface of loose rocks. Many kinds of sea-slugs exactly resemble the surface on which they rest: the sea-lemon (*Doris*) is pale yellow with chestnut mottling, and looks merely like a thicker patch of pale yellow sponge growing against mottled colonies of sea-squirts and patches of pink and red seaweeds. Another kind of sea-slug is green, and is found only on green seaweed.

The chameleon prawn, *Hippolyte*, exactly resembles the colour of the weed to which it clings motionless during the daylight hours, whether it be green, red, or brown. In the deep rock pools prawns cling among the weeds, invisible unless disturbed, and in a sandy pool the shrimps, pressed flat against the bottom or buried up to the eyes, can be detected only by a skilled observer: or they may streak across the pool only to vanish again as they settle.

Many shore fish show a wonderful blending of tone and pattern with the setting in which one finds them. The blenny and the pogge are examples. These, and many other fish, together with shrimps, prawns, and their like, can rapidly adjust their tone, colour, and sometimes also their pattern with that of their environment. All these creatures see their background in some way—that is, the general appearance at and rather above their eye level—and unconsciously or automatically respond by adjusting their tone and colour thereto. This faculty, known as colour change, is more fully described in later chapters.

The flat fish found off-shore are particularly noted for their remarkable changes of colour and pattern, the brill and turbot being the most accomplished in this respect. These fish move about the sea bottom during their growth phases, and in search of food. Young flat fish inhabit sandy inshore grounds, with which they tone by means of their conspicuously white-spotted and patterned skin. As they migrate to the adult feeding grounds they take on the greyish-brown colour of the muddy bottom, or other tones, according to locality.

The sea-hare (*Aplysia*) provides a remarkable story of colour changes. It is of the same nature as a large garden snail, but with only the remains of a shell buried in a hump on its back. The sea-hare resembles an animated piece of seaweed rather than a highly developed mollusc. Where we expect a head and " horns " there is a snout with curling, seaweed-like fronds, and other softly curving lobes surround its hump. It clings to the weed in seaweed-like attitudes for hours at a time, being in perfect colour harmony meanwhile. Adult sea-hares are dark brown, with green, purple, or olive tints, with lighter spangles here and there, and are very glossy. Among the curves and purple shadows of dark oar-weed or on toothed wrack they are difficult to detect. (Plate 4.)

Sea-hares live below low-water mark, but in spring and early summer many come up to the shore and deposit their spawn on the rocks or weed. When larvæ hatch from the spawn they are carried out to sea, develop as transparent creatures among the drifting surface population (plankton), and at a certain age sink to the sea floor and begin to feed and shelter amongst the weed. Specimens of sea-hares dredged from various depths show that the very young feed mainly on a rosy-red weed (*Delesseria sanguinea*), whose colour they resemble exactly. Next, when about a month older, they are found further inshore, resembling and feeding on a red-brown weed (*Iridoea edulis*). They pass later to a deep red-brown weed, and finally to the olive and purple-brown wracks and oar-weeds in a zone below low-tide mark. Professor Garstang kept young sea-hares through all these stages, and found that, although they were kept on weed of uniform colour, they still showed the varied colours natural to their developmental stages. So in nature the animal seeks out and feeds amongst the weed which tones with its own colour.

Among spider crabs are many instances of what appears to be deliberate protective disguise. Spider crabs are slow-moving creatures with delicate, easily broken legs, and their disguise undoubtedly helps the smaller kinds at least to survive. The back and legs of these creatures bear spines and small hooks, and on these the crab hangs suitable materials for disguise. It is a quaint and pretty sight to see one of these crabs with bits of bright red and green weed stuck here and there on its shell. When resting on a stone amidst a cluster of weeds from which it took its disguise the crab is impossible to detect without the closest scrutiny.

Experiments show that spider crabs definitely select a camouflage suitable to their immediate case. One kind, collected from a region of red seaweed and clothed in this, was placed in a bowl of green seaweed. It removed the red weed from its spines, took green weed, tore it up with its pincers, and firmly pressed the green pieces into position on its spines. Specimens of another kind of spider crab which, when discovered, were weed-dressed, were put amongst quite different materials, such as small shells and gravel, or stones on which grew tufts of sea-firs. All clothed themselves suitably until quite hidden in their new setting. Other spider crabs plant gardens of sponges and weeds on their backs.

In contrast to the harmless self-effacement of the spider crabs is the grim camouflage of the angler fish, which results in the capture of small prey. This fish lies in a hollow it makes for itself in the mud of the sea bottom, and keeps quite still, its tone and pattern closely matching its surroundings. It has a huge flat head tapering to an insignificant body whose outline is obscured by tags of skin along the sides. The foremost supporting ray of the angler's dorsal fin is very long and has a tassel of skin at its tip. This "fishing-rod" generally lies flat along the angler's back, but at the approach of a small fish the angler raises it above its head and jerks it to and fro, while the tassel wriggles as though it were a bunch of little worms. The fish swims near to inspect this bait, and in a second the angler's vast mouth opens and engulfs it. (Plate 8.)

An intriguing optical effect is produced by certain squids, animals capable of very rapid colour changes. They show dark and light horizontal stripes while swimming, which give an illusion of streaks of water, but when they come to rest these stripes vanish and are replaced by vertical bands suggesting weed with its undulating surface alternately in light and shade. Among fishes of the coral reefs, the blue-striped grunts while swimming show tones from gold to deep brown, but when at rest dark vertical bands appear on their sides.

The foregoing are characteristic instances of the likeness between animals and their sea-floor environment. Bottom-living creatures are in general opaque, and bear patterns and markings of some kind. Often they have sculptured outlines. All this is in keeping with the general effect of rocks, gravel, speckled sand, coloured weeds of irregular shapes, and constantly changing motion and shadow among the weeds. Uniform colours, whether pale or bright, are found only among the relatively inedible sponges, starfish, anemones, and their kin, or in molluscs with thick protective shells.

Above the sea bottom, the creatures assume self-colours and water-shades, and in the well-lighted surface waters transparency (as in arrow worms, young stages of crabs, starfish, etc.), or a mere hint of colour, is the cue for invisibility.

LIGHT REGULATING LIVING-DEPTH

So much for conditions during the day, when animals can see and be seen. As to the "seeing" of marine animals, all the modes known among the land fauna hold good for sea creatures—general sensitivity to light, more local and acute perception by means of eye-spots, and real eyes of many types. In another chapter we consider more carefully what the eyes of fish can see. A distinction must be made between "seeing" and "perceiving", and the question of interpreting what is seen is also involved. For present purposes we may say that light is one of the most important conditions governing the behaviour of the smaller freely-moving sea animals. Large, strong creatures such as whales and certain fish may range freely from depth to surface at any time, but the majority are restricted. For each there is a condition of strong or weak light most suitable to its well-being, and in this quality of light it is maintained by its internal mechanisms. Light causes photochemical reactions to take place within the living creature; if it wanders upwards towards a region of too strong light, the reactions increase and drive the animal downwards; or if it moves towards too dim a light region, the photochemical reactions are such as to direct it upwards. In the same way, a moth is compelled to fly towards a localised source of light, in this case to its detriment, but the conditions are unnatural.

Thus during the hours of daylight the creatures, even the micro-plant population, are found at varying depths below the surface, each at the depth which gives it the best light conditions : few can stand the strong light of the surface itself. As dusk falls, many migrate upwards, following the quality of light that suits them. Hence some kinds of fishing can be done only at night : herring and other food fishes come to the surface then, following the hordes of lesser creatures which nourish them. Hake, flatfish, and rays, which are found at or near the bottom in daytime, become active in the water above during the night. During the hours of darkness there tends to be a general intermingling of the animal zones, for when the stimulus of light is removed, all have freedom of movement at any level, and only when light appears again is each type directed once more to the depth suitable to itself.*

Camouflage depending on colour can be effective only during

* How great is the difference in light intensity, and how important to transparent creatures such as jellyfish, can be gathered from figures given by F. S. Russel. The medusa *Cosmetira pilosella* is most abundant in daytime at a depth of about 25 metres. Here the light intensity on Sept. 3, 1925, was 470 metre-candles at a depth of 27·2 metres. The actual intensity at this depth in summer was not measured, but it may be taken as not more than 2,000 metre-candles. In nature, this is quite the highest light intensity this jellyfish would experience. Contrast this with the light at the surface, which would be 80,000 metre-candles at least.

the hours of daylight. Then, for example, the chameleon prawn *Hippolyte* is opaque and perfectly tones in colour with the weed to which it clings. When darkness falls it becomes transparent and tinted with sapphire-blue. This is usually thought of as a casting-off of protective disguise, but possibly *Hippolyte* merely assumes a nocturnal cloak of invisibility in which it becomes active and feeds. Unfortunately our eyes cannot see the natural effect in the night sea.

Any animal that hunts by normal sight must do so during the daylight. Hence the wrasse, a fish which by day feeds on crabs,

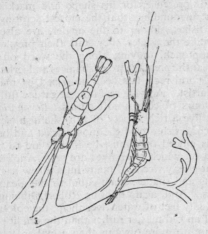

FIG. 2.—Chameleon prawns resting on seaweed (about twice natural size).

shrimps, and shellfish, by night lies about in the rock crevices and "sleeps". The blue-green sunfish of tropical waters certainly hunts by sight. Experiments show that the small fish which are its prey are capable of background adaptation, and are to a definite extent protected from the sunfish if suitably adjusted in colour.

No reference to camouflage in the sea can be complete without mention of the life of tropical and sub-tropical waters. The Sargasso Sea has great patches of weed floating at the surface, with a fauna all its own. Sargassum weed takes the form of stems and notched leaves, with stalked fruits here and there. The shells of various encrusting animals form light spots on the weed. The creatures sheltering in the weed wear a yellow livery with irregular brown markings and white spots, and until shaken out of the weed they remain unnoticed. Apart from their colour harmony, many have little tags or streamers or knobs which blend their form with that of the weed. The numerous pipe-fishes have a long, narrow body like a thick piece of seaweed stem.

Robert Gibbings describes how from a bucketful of seaweed he shook at least two dozen fish and ten times as many crabs, shrimps, and worms. The Sargasso fish itself is shown in his woodcut. "Only by shaking the Sargasso fish from the weed was it possible to discover his presence, for his shape and markings blended so well with his surroundings that the closest scrutiny failed to find him." Frog fishes, similar to the angler, are also found in the weed, but, unlike the angler, they stalk their prey with steady and determined approach, moving along the weed on their flippers. When quite near the prey, the frog fish raises and jerks its fishing-rod.

The life of coral reefs has been described by many a traveller, scientist, and artist. A living reef is a sea garden full of the delicate and vivid colours of corals, soft corals (*Alcyonaria*), and weeds, among which live a rich variety of fish, shellfish, sea urchins, and so on. The coral fish are of the most varied and brilliant colours imaginable, as indeed they must be if they are to blend with the rainbow stage on which their lives are set. Another point to be realised is that glossy weeds of many hues throw back most vividly coloured lights and shades, quite equal to the gleam and flash of the fish's sides. And, again quoting Robert Gibbings, " . . . with a dozen or twenty feet of water over them, the colours take on the mellowness of an old master rather than the crudity of a new one, and the fish are no more obvious than a mallard among reeds, or a butterfly at rest in a garden ".

From the wealth of examples a few may be chosen. In the sea around the Bermuda reef is found the great surgeon fish, so called on account of the sharp stylet in its tail-fin. During his submarine researches Longley observed this fish to be black almost all over when near the sea bottom, but when it swims upwards, clear of the reef face and into open water, it takes on a delicate blue-grey which renders it barely visible. Gibbings writes, "It seems, at first thought, impossible that emerald-green fish should find adequate cover among the petals of pink coral, but then emerald green is the complementary colour of that particular shade of pink, and the fish is thereby absorbed into its shadows ".

The eye of a fish is likely to be a vulnerable and conspicuous point, and is often camouflaged. Among the Tahiti reefs there lives the "Four Eye", whose true eye is obscured by a vertical dark stripe, while a large black-and-white "eye" is marked on each side close to the base of the tail. If alarmed, the "Four Eye" swims backwards, and usually gets safely into shelter. The common sea-horse is not easy to see among its weed, but in areas of the Australian reef is found a kind of sea-horse, the "sea dragon" whose already strange outline is further obscured by leaf-like out-growths, until it cannot be distinguished from the weed in which it lives.

SELF-LUMINOUS ANIMALS

The consideration of light and colour in the sea brings us to the light produced by marine animals themselves. Phosphorescence,—to use the best-known term for such light, is widespread among sea animals. The bright, cold light which they emit, though invisible in the far more powerful light of day, in darkness appears very similar to that g.ven out by yellow phosphorus and by commercial barium and calcium sulphides.

Dead animals may also seem to give out light, but this is still the result of a living process, for the light results from the action of bacteria carrying out the work of decomposition. Dead fish, which are rich in phosphorus, can give a startling and uncanny display on a dark night, appearing as a patch of silvery light of no immedi-ately identifiable origin. Such material gives off a continuous flood of light, as do certain living fungi and living fish. But this is an exception : in nearly all luminous animals the light is inter-mittent ; a stimulus of some kind is needed to produce it, and when the stimulus passes the light disappears.

In Britain, the countryman has two chances of seeing the effect of animal light. On a hedge-bank or a down, especially during a still night in summer, resembling small stars which have dropped to earth here and there, will be found glow-worms, the female of a dull-coloured hedge beetle.* More rarely a luminous centipede runs by. In the tropics may be seen the luminous fireflies (*Photinus* and *Photurus*), tiny winged beetles which dance in the air. In the Southern States of U.S.A. there is a kind of fly which goes by the name of the automobile bug, for at night it shows a white light in front of its head and a ruby light at the rear.

At various times dwellers by the sea have often seen a brilliant, scintillating light playing upon the surface, off our own coasts particu-larly in summer and autumn. It is an unforgettable experience to

* *Lampyrus :* the male has only two tiny spots of light at the end of the body.

take a rowing-boat out on a dark night and watch the silvery trail in the wake of the boat, the splashes of light made as the oars break from the water, and the shining gems that drop from them into the dark sea. As well as this surface " burning of the sea ", sailors, especially in the Mediterranean and warmer oceans, sometimes find the night waters lighted to some depth by globes of white fire which wax and wane as a shoal of jellyfish float by, or see a sudden streak of light caused by the rush of some luminous fish or squid.

The production of light by luminous creatures, a process peculiar to themselves, is best named " bio-luminescence ". It is the result of a form of oxidation or combustion. But while, in such a process, it is usual for energy to be released in the form of heat as well as light (candle, fire, electric light are all " warm " lights), when light is produced in animals all the energy is released as light and none wasted in the form of heat. Hence the term " cold light ". The light-producing material found in animals is named luciferin. When luciferin combines with oxygen, light results. The enzyme or catalyst which effects this oxidation of luciferin is called luciferase. The exact nature of the enzyme varies from one type of creature to another, as does the exact quality of the light to which each gives rise. To the human eye, most kinds of animal light appear silvery, pale green, or pale violet.

Luciferin is nearly always found in the form of granules. These are scattered through the whole substance of certain tiny animals, so that their whole body lights up, as in the protozoan *Noctiluca* (Light of the night). Just visible without a microscope, *Noctiluca* occurs in incalculable numbers in the plankton during the summer months, and much of the scintillating surface-light is caused by the waxing and waning of these tiny points of light.

In several animals a luminous slime is produced at the surface and oxidised in the presence of sea-water. Some of the lower Crustacea produce this slime at certain points only, others throw it off over the whole body as a luminous veil. Many people are familiar with the cylindrical burrows bored in marl or in sandstone by the piddock (*Pholas*), a bivalve mollusc. The piddock produces quite a brilliant light, of blue-green colour, on five parts of its skin. Other creatures light up over their whole body, as does the big marine worm *Chaetopterus*, which lives concealed in a parchment-like tube buried in mud, or the sea pen, which occurs in fairly deep water off the coast of Scotland. *Chaetopterus* tubes are dredged up in Plymouth Sound for study at the Marine Biological Laboratory. If the worms are taken into a dark room, removed from their tube, and gently stroked with a paint-brush, waves of pale violet or green light pass over the body. Another marine worm (*Heteronereis*), a powerful swimmer, comes up to the surface at night during the breeding season. As one looks over the side of a rowing-boat into the dark sea it suddenly appears from the depths as a wavering light, shoots swiftly to the surface as a white flash, and as quickly descends below.

Besides these animals which produce light here and there, or all over the surface of the body, there are others with definite "light organs" or self-luminous torches in which the production of light is concentrated and amplified. Light organs are found in rapid swimmers with good eyesight—squids, cuttle-fish, fish, prawns, and the prawn-like krill or Euphausiids. Some kinds of squid have most elaborate organs, and so do certain deep-sea cuttles, which have over twenty lamps. One has a pair of sky-blue lamps near its eyes, white lamps down each side, and a pair of red lamps at the rear. The artificial lighting system of the krill is specially well known to fishermen, as these small creatures, about an inch and a half long, are present in countless myriads in the plankton of the northern seas, and are of immense importance as food for edible fish. Krill are transparent save for their large black eyes and tiny red pigment spots. Along the sides of the body and under the tail are numerous lamps, which light up or go out according to a nervous impulse from the animal. Russel says that it is just possible to read a newspaper by the light from half a dozen krill in a jar of sea-water.

This voluntary emission of light may be compared with the voltage discharge from the electric organs of torpedo and electric ray, which have a nervous generating mechanism. Deeper studies of both these phenomena are obviously important, since they might shed light on the nature and action of our own "nervous energy".

The light organs of all these creatures are fairly similar in plan. Light is produced in a layer of luminous cells: in front is a lens which serves to focus and transmit the light, and is covered by a protective transparent skin. The luminous cells are backed by a reflector, and light is prevented from escaping from the back of the organ by a coat of dark pigment. The oxygen necessary for light production is conveyed by the bloodstream.

How are we to interpret this production of animal light? It appears to serve no useful purpose in many cases—the piddock in its burrow, the *Chaetopterus* worm in its tube in the mud, jellyfish which are avoided on account of their stinging habits, and *Noctiluca* which is swallowed wholesale. In other cases, light production may have its uses. There is no doubt that a lamp hung over the side of a boat attracts various sea creatures. The deep sea angler fish has a luminous bait, and to test its efficiency Prof. Herdman let down two nets on the sea bottom for half an hour at night, one with lamps at its entrance, the other without. There was a big catch in the lighted net and practically none in the other.

It is tempting to think that in the dim-lit waters certain prawns and fish make use of their own artificial light, taking lanterns with them in their search of food. A sudden discharge of light may, on the other hand, serve to ward off a pursuer.

Much has been written of the very deep sea with the strange fish that inhabit it and their glimmering of phosphorescent light amidst the gloom. Luminous fish are not, however, especially common in the deep sea, but belong mostly to the upper 500 metres of the warmer seas. Perhaps at great depths the pressure is such that sufficient oxygenation cannot take place for the production of light.

The fact that in the fireflies, glow-worms, and some kinds of worms and fish light is produced chiefly or solely at the breeding season suggests that it may serve as a recognition signal. In any case, it accompanies the special physiological condition of the animal at that period.

It seems probable that the production of luminosity is one of the many chemical activities which accompany the life process and take the form of the emission of radiations. The fact that the electro-magnetic radiations concerned happen to be visible to the human eye, and presumably to the eyes of animals, may not be of any special significance, except perhaps in creatures whose light production has become specialised in light organs. The spectrum of light, for example, from *Cypridina* (one of the lower Crustacea) is a broad band with a maximum at 4800 Å., well within the range of human vision. Other electro-magnetic waves—Gurwitch's mitogenetic rays—which are given off when plant cells divide, are of wave-length about 2000 Å., and are invisible to the human observer.

In passing, we may note that the human eye may be activated so that it becomes sensitive to wave-lengths above and below the normal spectrum. If a dicyanin screen is looked through by diffuse daylight it becomes activated in a manner which allows it to record wave-lengths not normally perceived. The interpretation of such results, which have been noticed by several observers, remains as yet a matter of doubt. A simple experiment will quickly show how the eyes may be sensitised to certain colours, so that they appear more vivid. If a clear solution of blue, for example, is put into a glass, the glass is held up to the light, and the observer looks at it for a minute or so, then looks out at the scenery, yellow and red colours appear far more vivid than usual.

SIMPLE RECIPE FOR MAKING A LUMINOUS MATERIAL *

Heat a few oyster shells in the fire until they become white, and then heat them to a red heat in an old tin with twice their weight of sulphur for a few hours. After exposure to strong light, the resultant compound will become luminous.

CHAPTER V

CAMOUFLAGE OF INSECTS AND SPIDERS: MIMICRY

MOST insects make their home amongst plants and are nourished by feeding on some part of the plant body. Many insects are restricted to one kind of plant food only; for example, caterpillars of the mullein moth feed only on mullein leaves, and almost every kind of fruit blossom is attacked by its own species of weevil. A general resemblance between the insect and the plant which provides food, shelter, or both, seems quite natural and is a very usual state of affairs. But very detailed cryptic camouflage is also typical of many insects, involving colour, form, and behaviour.

GRASSHOPPERS

Grasshoppers are past masters in the art of camouflage. They are extremely difficult to locate when they settle after a leap. Grasshoppers have a covering of many fine plates, some of which are smooth and throw off high lights that break the outline here and there. At other places ridges interrupt an otherwise smooth surface, often giving the appearance of the veins on a leaf or ribs on a stem. A grasshopper resting on a blade of grass is a solid, angular form, yet by many subtleties of colour and sculpturing it merges with the thin strip of green. The upper surface of one of the common British grasshoppers is bright green, and a central darker ridge prevents undue reflection of light. Brownish-green wing-covers, slightly arched, catch the light and, being translucent, appear like fallen leaf-scales, or suggest the paler region where a grass-blade joins the stem. The grasshopper's sloping "face"

* *Newnes' Practical Mechanics*, Jan. 1937.

and underside are yellow-green, following the usual counter-shading plan of darker colour above and paler below. The green abdomen ends not abruptly, but almost imperceptibly in a cluster of earth-brown tapering points; in side view, black patches break up the green, so that one appears to be looking at a number of short vertical lengths of grass-blade with dark shadows between. The thighs have a green upper surface, changing to chestnut brown below. A strong ridge along the top gives the effect of a raised leaf-vein, while the broad outer surface of the thigh has fine herring-bone markings which prevent it appearing as a single ovoid area. It is very usual in grasshoppers for a bold pattern to continue unbroken across the body and bent thighs, a device which deflects attention from the shape of these large structures.

On the dry brown earth of a field are to be seen grasshoppers which look exactly like scraps of dead leaf or twig. They are earth-brown, with fawn and tawny markings just the shape and colour of scraps of straw. Prominent ridges around the knees give a gnarled effect, and the sides of the body are mottled grey, cream, and chestnut. One would not suspect these scraps of debris of being living insects able to leap two or three feet at a second's notice.

British grasshoppers hatch from eggs in early summer, and may be found on herbage by the wayside, in the meadow, or on cliff or moor. Most kinds have two broods in the year, and in late autumn they die off, leaving eggs buried in the ground. The first young grasshoppers grow up in a world of vivid green leaves, and this green is their dominant colour. From the time of hay harvest onwards, paler greens and straw colours are prominent, and the grasshoppers are clothed likewise. Many earth-coloured types occur in places where earth is exposed. On heaths and moors where it is the practice to burn the bracken, exist wide areas of black ground with charred stumps and grey ashes, and here the grasshoppers are black with grey and white markings.

Grasshoppers grow rather slowly, and it is the immature forms which react to radiations from their environment. Describing a grasshopper from the Russian Steppes, Mrs. H. H. Brindley writes, " In June, while the grass is still fresh and green, the Tryxalids are green, with a silvery bloom shading into purple on the antennae and margins of the elytra. They are indistinguishable among the blades and purple panicles of the grass. In August, when the herbage becomes dried and yellow, the grasshoppers still feed in the same spots, but now they are brown and scorched-looking, in the perfect similitude of bits of straw.''

Grasshoppers living in desert conditions have their own camouflage devices. The vivid light casts strong shadows, especially at the junction of thigh with body. In a stony desert of Algeria is to be found a grasshopper which in texture, colour, and rounded outlines has an appearance identical with the bare, sunlit pebbles amongst which it crouches. A fringe of hairs prevents the occurrence of the tell-tale shadow between thigh and body. An Australian grasshopper simulates a twig. It takes up a strange position, head downwards on a branch, with feet, legs, and body applied flat to the surface. The stiff wing-covers (elytra) are raised and stand out at an angle, just like a twig.

BUTTERFLIES AND MOTHS

Butterflies and moths, both in their mature and developing stages, offer an infinite range of camouflage examples. In Britain a common grey-green lichen (*Usnea barbata*), which grows in tufts on trees in the West Country and elsewhere, serves as home and food for the caterpillar of the Brussels Lace Moth (*Cleora lichenaria*). The caterpillar blends exactly with the lichen; only by the merest chance would it be discovered. The Merveille-du-jour is an exquisitely coloured moth with an irregular pattern of pale green and grey, and darker patches like shadows. During the daytime it rests on lichen of exactly these tones and colours, and is almost impossible to detect.

There are moths that in all three different phases of existence—larva, pupa, and winged imago—blend perfectly with their natural setting. The Oak Beauty Moth rests by day, with wings spread, on the trunk of an oak tree. Oak bark has its own special texture, colour, and pattern. On the moth's wings are areas which appear identical with the bark and merge with it completely, but other areas contrast strongly and stand out conspicuously, so breaking up the outline of the spread wings. The pupa of the Oak Beauty has the colours of the earth in which it shelters. The larva resembles the twigs of the oak on whose leaves it feeds. The body is light brown, and the skin has ridges and folds like those of the twig. The head has a knobbly, irregular appearance. The larva spends most of the day still and rigid, clasping the stem with its rear feet, its body projecting outwards in twig fashion. Such larvae are detected only if they move, or are touched before one suspects their presence.

The wings of butterflies offer great opportunities for camouflage artistry. Often the upper surfaces of both wings are brightly coloured, while the lower surfaces have a cryptic colour scheme.

When the butterfly alights, the wings of left and right sides are folded together vertically over its back, so that the under surfaces alone are visible. Here are seen mottled colourings in shades of brown and grey, suggesting bark, dead leaves, or stone. The margins of the wings, which in silhouette tend to be the most clearly defined part, are usually chequered or banded, a type of marking which suggests three-dimensional relief, such as the wavy edge of bark. The recognisable outline of a pair of wings is often abolished by some striking pattern which runs right across the upper and lower wing of the same side. In the Blood-vein Moth (*Timandra amata*) a vertical red stripe is present on either side; it divides the wing areas so effectively that one appears to be looking at random scraps of pale leaf on a carpet of fallen leaves.

The classical example of the Dead Leaf Butterfly of India and Ceylon (*Kallima*) is a perfect instance of camouflage by reason of colour, shape, and posture. The butterfly is large, the upper surface of the wings of rich purple crossed by a band of orange. In flight it is quite a striking object, but when it suddenly alights on a bush it vanishes from sight. The folded wings are leaf-shaped, with a pointed tip, and stalk-like projection at the base. The tip of this "stalk" is laid against a twig, so completing the illusion of a dead leaf still attached to its branch. The under surface of the wings is dark brown, spots of decay being indicated here and there in black; running up the centre is a dark line suggesting the mid-rib of the leaf.

Several butterflies have the interesting habit of alighting in such a position that their wings cast the minimum of shadow. The broad surface of the folded wings, held over the body in the manner of a sail, tends to cast a conspicuous shadow unless the butterfly orientates itself parallel to the direction of the sun. Thus placed, there may be no shadow at all, or at most a thin black line, which, to a passing bird, does not suggest a butterfly at rest. The Grayling (*Satyrus semeli*) often rests on the bare ground with folded wings. It has a habit of tilting the wings over to one side, with the result that their cryptic pattern is fully exposed. The shadows cast by the raised wing-veins break the light wing-surface into multiple areas.

A significant production of harmonising colour occurs once during the life of various butterflies—namely, at the critical stage when the colours of the pupa or chrysalis are determined. The pupa of the Cabbage White butterfly is closely adjusted in colour, tone, and pattern to the bark, wall or fence to which it is moored, or, as is often the case in the first brood, to the green colour of the food plant. This colour adjustment is due to the highly-developed sensitivity of the caterpillar's eyes to the reflected light coming from the background on which it takes up its position just before pupation occurs. This resting period extends over almost exactly four days (D. Moore). Experiments made by covering the caterpillar's eyes with transparent dyes of different colours prove that the eyes, and not the skin as a whole, are the receptors concerned. The small Tortoise-shell and the Peacock butterfly also have pupæ which show marked harmony with the colour of their surroundings. The colour of the pupa is also affected by the temperature at which the critical change occurs.

There are caterpillars whose colour is determined by their surroundings. In various moth families (Noctuids, Sphingiids, and Geometers) the caterpillars may be green or brown, according to circumstances. Lappet Moth larvæ when young can adjust their colour and pattern, and the Cabbage Moth (*Mamestra brassicae*) can produce larvæ of several colour varieties.

Some caterpillars have the surprising habit of assuming a terrifying " mask " if disturbed or alarmed. The Puss Moth larva is famous for such behaviour. Izaak Walton describes him accurately, " Nay, the very colours of caterpillars are, as one has observed, very elegant and beautiful. I shall, for a taste of the rest, describe one of them; which I will, some time the next month, show you feeding on a willow tree; and you shall find him punctually to answer this very description: his lips and mouth somewhat yellow; his eyes black as jet; his forehead purple; his feet and hinder parts green; his tail two-forked and blacked; the whole body stained with a kind of red spots, which run along the neck and shoulder blade, not unlike the form of St. Andrew's Cross, or the letter X, made thus cross-wise, and a white line drawn down his back to his tail; all which add much beauty to his whole body."

If the Puss Moth caterpillar is disturbed, it withdraws its head slightly and brings into view parts of the body which are usually concealed. Eltringham gives a vivid description of the result, " . . . a dreadful face appears, red and furious, two large coal-black eyes stare at the intruder, whilst the forked tail rises up to battle and from its points issue two wicked-looking scarlet threads which twist and wriggle like venomous worms ". The terrifying mask is purely a bluff, but the thread-like whips can be put to good account if the parasitic ichneumon fly makes an attack; it is often beaten off, sometimes with damaged wings.

Even more singular is the behaviour of some foreign Hawk Moth larvæ. One, a native of Para (*Leucorhampha ornatus*), when at rest resembles a broken twig. It grips a branch by means of two pairs of claspers, and its body, coloured like bark encrusted with lichen, projects stiffly at an angle. If alarmed, the larva becomes transformed. It reveals its underside, and puffs out the thoracic segments, producing the effect of the head and neck of a small but formidable snake having yellow, black-edged scales, black eyes, and a broad band of dark green along its underside. The effect is enhanced by a side-to-side swaying movement which fascinates and terrifies an animal that witnesses the display.

The Praying Mantis

The Praying Mantis is a formidable example of camouflage for aggression. The insect gets its name from the attitude it assumes when preparing to capture prey. The long, powerful joint at the end of the foreleg can act like the blade of a penknife, being half opened, then closing swiftly against its sheath, with the prey trapped between. In the " praying " attitude the mantis waits, quite still, with uplifted forelegs and half-opened " blades ". It cannot strike until the prey comes really close, but its presence remains unsuspected because of resemblance to leaf or flower.

Many kinds of mantis wait beside a flower whose petals they resemble in shape and colour. There is an Indian mantis which forms an accurate copy of a nectar-yielding flower, and feeds on the insects that alight for nectar. Mantids are found commonly in the eastern and southern regions of the U.S.A., and destroy many insects harmful to flowers, as well as a certain number of bees. There are others that resemble twigs or leaves. Kingston observed a leaf mantis which clung to bark, for the most part remaining quite still, but from time to time making irregular varied movements like those of a leaf fluttering in a sudden breeze.

Caddis Larvæ

The caddis larvæ of ponds and slow-moving streams provide a homely but intriguing study in camouflage. These soft-bodied, edible insects weave for themselves a tube of silk into which they fasten scraps of twig or leaf, tiny shells, pieces of fine gravel, and suchlike materials gathered from the bottom of the pond. They may bite pieces of suitable shape from the living leaves of water plants and weld them into a light, pliable tube with the aid of silk spun in their mouths. The caddis larvæ crawl about with only their head end exposed, and at the approach of danger withdraw safe within their portable houses. How deceptive these tubes are may be realised from a single example. Standing on the edge of an artificial pond and looking down its sloping concrete sides, scraps of twig were observed resting here and there on the slope, or floating at the surface. The water was quite still—yet some of the twigs moved slowly about ! These moving twigs were caddis larvæ browsing in minute green stuff on the concrete sides.

STICK INSECTS

A visitor to the South of France tells how he was taken up to a rose-bush and shown a number of green stick insects clinging among the leaves. Their bodies were just like the smooth green stems of the rose-bush, or, the partly rotted leaves seen from various angles. Their legs were so slender as to escape notice, or to pass for a raised leaf-vein catching the light. Even after distinguishing the insects when quite close to them, it was impossible to detect them at a yard's distance. They remained quite still the whole time.

Anyone who keeps stick insects for the first time knows the curious experience of shutting them carefully in a cage at night, clinging to leafy shoots of privet, then opening the cage next morning and thinking every single one has escaped. After the first shock, a careful look round reveals first one, then another, until all are accounted for, still in the cage. The insects fed and moved about during the night: then they "froze" into daytime attitudes different from those in which they were left the night before, and the eye had to begin all over again to see through the illusion. The body of the stick insect is the conspicuous "twig"—the head just makes a slightly irregular finish at one end, the long, angular legs appear as leaves seen edge on, or as leaf-veins. Unless strongly disturbed, stick insects remain motionless during the daylight hours, in a cataleptic state. Occasionally the long legs will move, so that the body sways from side to side like a leaf caught in a random current of air. At night they move about and feed, and may travel a considerable distance on their long legs.

Stick insects are entirely defenceless, and animals find them good to eat. Their shape, colour, harmony, and immobility often help them to escape from insect-eaters, particularly birds and lizards, their main enemies.

There are several colour forms: green, brown, and intermediate shades. All forms have several pigments present as granules in the cells of the skin: these are orange and yellow lipochromes, brown melanin, and a red and green pigment. According to the colour-tone of the bush, hedge, or tree where the insects take up their home, the amounts of the various pigments increase or decrease within a short time until adjustment is complete (morphological colour change).

At the same time each colour form, with the exception of the green one, varies in the depth and quality of its colour, according to passing circumstance. The insects are paler by day and darker by night. In moist air they become darker in something under an hour, while in dry air they become paler in from one to two hours. The walls of the air-carrying tracheal tubes act as receptors for the moisture content of the air, the stimulus being conveyed from them to the nervous system. Temperature and oxygen content of the air also affect the colour tone.

Stick insects respond to a light background (white or light yellow) by becoming pale, and to a dark background (black or red) by becoming darker. Atzler showed that the lower part of the insect's eye, which receives light reflected from the background, is responsible for adjustment of body colour to background colour. She also showed that both the quick temporary adjustments (physiological colour change) to day and night, moisture, temporary resting-place, and so on—changes due to the spreading out or knotting up of the brown or orange pigments—and the slower, more permanent changes caused by making or withdrawing various pigments (morphological colour change)—are regulated by a hormone released by a gland in the insect's head, activated through the brain. The eyes are receptors for both direct and reflected light, the antennæ are mainly concerned with reception of temperature stimuli, and the tracheæ with those of moisture.

Prof. Giersburg, under whom the work was done, considers that these two kinds of colour change, morphological and physiological, are two aspects of the same process. Continued stimulation of the colour-change centre in the brain results in an increase of hormone content in the blood, leading to the development of extra pigment.

SPIDERS

Two kinds of small spider make their home in flowers. One of these flower-spiders (*Misumena calycina*) may be white or canary-yellow; it can change from one colour to the other in less than a week. The flowers of leguminous plants are a favourite haunt of these flower-spiders. One only detects them by chance, as, for instance, when a canary-coloured spider has descended from a flowering laburnum to capture prey on a green plant of the herbage below, or when after bringing a bunch of meadow flowers indoors, a flower-bud seems for a moment to become animated and runs across the table, revealing the presence of the spider.

Another species (*M. vatia*) was found to change its colour during the summer according to the flowers it chose to frequent. In

June and July these spiders were found in ox-eye daisies, where they were all white. In late July and early August the spiders were mostly found in Golden Rod, and some of them had become yellow, while by mid-August and September all had become pale or dark yellow.

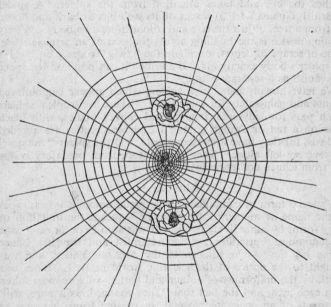

Fig. 3.—Web camouflage. The Asiatic spider (*Cyclosa mulmeinensis* Thor.) which makes false hubs of silk on its web, in the centre of which bundles of debris are placed of about the same size as the spider itself. A bird is likely to peck at one of these, leaving the spider unharmed.

The other genus of flower-spiders (*Thomisus onustus*) is pink, and usually found among heather blooms. It can change colour to a limited extent. There is an elegant garden spider (*Aranea reaumuri*), coloured bright green and found amongst grass, which can within forty-eight hours take on a bark-brown colour.

Among web-building spiders are some whose camouflage prevents the opaque body from presenting too conspicuous a contrast to the web itself. The web or snare is often almost invisible, but the spider can be clearly seen, and is liable to attack from a passing bird. One kind of spider (*Cyclosa* sp.) builds one or two false hubs of silk on its web, and at the centre of each places a bundle of scraps about the same size as its own body. Another decorates its web with a bold zig-zag or spiral of thick white silk, which catches the eye and takes attention from the spider. A spider of British Guiana (*Azilia*) places on its web bits of bark and lichen cut from a tree, of just the size and colour of its own body. A very cunning device is the building across the web of an artificial twig, made of scraps of debris, leaving in the " twig " a space into which the spider's body exactly fits. If alarmed it can pop into the space and vanish as a separate entity.

We have already mentioned spiders which appear camouflaged as ants and gain safety for this reason. There are tropical spiders which pass for ladybirds, having oval convex bodies, with black spots on a red or orange ground. Ladybird beetles are avoided by birds, for they have a nauseous taste, and the spider " mimics " are severely left alone. They escape, too, from predatory wasps and from ichneumon parasites.

MIMICRY

A special form of camouflage, widespread amongst insects, goes by the name of mimicry. By mimicry is meant the imitation of living forms by other living forms. It was seen to occur on a wide scale amongst butterflies by the naturalist and traveller Bates, during his eleven-year sojourn in the Amazon Valley, and was brought to the notice of the scientific world in 1861. Bates was struck by the uniformity of colour and pattern of specimens taken from each area, and the fact that " they changed, as it were, with the touch of an enchanter's wand, in passing from one area to another ".

A famous instance is that of the family of Heliconias. These butterflies have long oval wings, coloured black and yellow. They go about in large companies, with slow, deliberate flight. They are inedible by birds and lizards on account of an evil-smelling fluid which they exude if attacked. A large catch of Heliconias, when examined closely, was found to contain species of two genera of butterflies belonging to another family, the Pieridae, whose near relatives look altogether different in colour and in wing-shape. The Pieridae are edible, but owing to their likeness to the nauseous Heliconias they escape attack.

This is a straightforward example. But Bates also made the puzzling discovery that species belonging to another unpalatable family of butterflies, the Ithomiidae, with a different warning colour scheme of their own, were found with the Heliconid livery of black and yellow. F. Muller, a naturalist living in Brazil, had also given much attention to the matter of butterfly mimicry, and his theory to explain such occurrences goes by the name of "Mullerian mimicry". In essence the theory is that insectivorous enemies, having learned to distinguish one nauseous type by its colour, may still attack other nauseous but differently coloured types. The latter will profit if they adopt the same colour scheme. As Prof. Poulton expresses it, "'Mullerian mimicry' is like the action of a group of powerful firms, which become still better known, at a lessened cost, by combined advertisement".

Fig. 4.—About three times natural size. On the right, an immature Membracid bug (*Rhynchota homoptera*) from British Guiana, which resembles an ant, together with the leaf it is carrying. The latter is shown left, and represents the species *Oecodoma cephalotes* from the same locality.

Typical of the complex phases of butterfly mimicry is the case of the *Danias* genus in Africa. Three species occur, all distasteful to birds, and all three are "copied" by the females of the swallow-tailed butterfly (*Papilio cenea*), while the males retain their normal shape and colour. All three female types, and the males, may hatch from eggs laid by a single female, a condition explicable under Mendelian heredity, but in origin none the less surprising. Breeding experiments show that environmental conditions may produce different types of female from a single batch of eggs. Dr. Van Someren found that as the result of knocking on the cage where larvæ had just pupated, the resulting butterflies showed a combination of male and female colour characteristics and shape. Such cases suggest great adaptability of certain forms to environ-

mental stimuli. Indeed, it seems reasonable to suppose tha
special physical and chemical conditions in certain localities hav
a direct action in producing brilliant colour schemes in responsiv
types, whether edible or inedible.

The easily recognised and relatively inedible ants serve as mode
to a variety of other creatures. In Guiana there lives a spide
which carries on its back the dead body of an ant. The spider i
concealed and protected by its burden, which is much larger tha

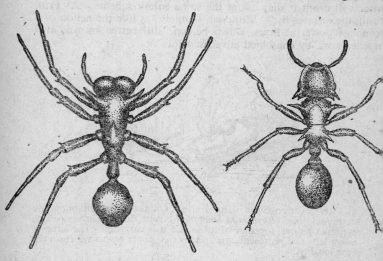

Figs. 5–6.—A South American Ant (*Cryptocerus atratus* L.) and a spider
(*Aphantochilus rogersi* Camb.) which mimics it.

the bearer, who passes for a member of the ant commune carrying
a dead individual. The leaf-cutting or Cooshie ants of Guiana
may be seen in procession, each carrying a jagged piece of leaf,
sail-like, on its back. Taking part in the procession, and only to
be distinguished by close observation, may be found an occasional
Membracid bug, also carrying a piece of leaf on its back. But it
is an artificial leaf, made by a thin green projection from the insect's
own body (Fig. 4).

Other creatures whose own natural shape would never allow
them to pass for ants, contrive a disguise in various ways. Two
separate kinds of spiders actually achieve an ant-like "figure";

one kind develops a "waist" from its cephalo-thorax, the other from its abdomen. A grasshopper from the Sudan has the tapering waist and rounded abdomen of the ant painted in black on its own pale ground colour. At least four other quite unrelated insects have a similar colour make-up that gives them a superficial likeness to ants. Mrs. Peckham describes a North American spider which develops the closest mimicry of ants in its movements. "Like an ant, when hunting for prey, the spider always zigzags from side to side in its walk, and holds up the second pair of legs in front of the head to simulate a pair of antennæ. Instead of standing still, as most spiders do, this spider keeps up an incessant twitching of the abdomen, pulling about its prey in different directions, the while beating it with its fore-legs and imitating to the life the restless movements of an ant when similarly engaged."

Most insectivorous animals avoid wasps, hornets and some of the many kinds of bees. The black and tawny colours and narrow transparent wings are the hall-marks of the warning livery of these Hymenoptera. A number of harmless, edible insects are found sailing under false colours of this type. The Hornet Clearwing moth and Lunar Hornet moth have the smooth slender body and wing-pattern of the dreaded hornet, and the Bee Hawk-moth has the short fluffy body and wing-pattern of a bumble bee. They all visit flowers in company with real wasps and bees. There are sixteen British species of Lepidoptera of the "clear-wing" pattern, whose mode of flight or appearance makes them almost indistinguishable from a stinging hymenopteran.

Among our British "hover flies" or Syrphids, some resemble wasps and some bees. If one watches the throng gathered around a clump of Michaelmas daisies, it is very hard to decide which is bee and which is hover fly. Only if one catches sight of a pair of long antennæ can an individual be certainly named a bee. *Volucella*, the "Bee-fly", habitually enters the nests of certain bees and wasps, where it lays eggs, and the resulting larvæ feed on debris, serving as scavengers.

Cott mentions a forest dragonfly which if captured behaves as though about to sting. These dragonflies bend the abdomen underneath the body and scrape its tip against the finger in a determined and menacing manner. A moth and a beetle occur which actually have a false sting which they put in and out if captured. There is a fly in British Guiana which is extremely like an Ichneumon wasp. This wasp has white-tipped antennæ, in constant vibration, and the fly has white fore-feet which are held up and waved gently to and fro.

Mimicry is a strange business, and raises questions for which no satisfactory scientific explanation is forthcoming. The subject is discussed again in a later chapter of this book. Mimicry can be seen in correct perspective only if considered in relation to the whole field of protective resemblance. We are accustomed to the fact of insects resembling bark, twigs, stones and so on. All the world over there are different kinds of insects which resemble dead leaves. Complete cryptic resemblance of an insect to a leaf is, however, quite as extraordinary as mimetic resemblance of a spider to an ant.

Supposing for the moment that insects are aware of tone, colour and pattern of inanimate objects in their immediate world, or of leaves and flowers which sway in the wind: why should they not also cognise the conspicuous, rapidly moving life which is equally a part of their environment? It is quite suitable for an insect of slow habits, living amongst lichen, to take on the appearance of lichen and survive by remaining still for the greater part of the daylight hours. Lichen does not move, and neither must the lichen insect. Leaf-dwelling insects are again creatures able to remain still for long periods of time, or to make occasional trembling movements like those of leaves. But amongst insects of active habits, what more suitable than to resemble some quickly moving, conspicuous model in the same environment, especially a model which visits the same place for food? It would be as unsuitable for a flying insect while in flight to resemble a leaf, as for a passive lichen-feeder to bear the disguise of a wasp.

CHAPTER VI

COLOUR CHANGE IN CUTTLEFISH, PRAWNS AND THEIR KIN

AMONG animals of the sea-shore, crabs, shrimps and prawns are the first to come to mind. For boys, crabs fulfil much the same need as do minnows and tadpoles in pond or stream, and shrimping has an appeal at all ages.

All these animals are classed among the Crustacea, a natural group of immense variety and number. In Crustacea the living skin secretes a protective covering of firm transparent material known as chitin. Chitin covers the entire surface, even the eyes, and is suitably hinged and jointed to allow for free movement. From time to time the unyielding exoskeleton of chitin is shed, the animal "moults", and rapid growth occurs before the new covering hardens.

In shrimps, prawns and tiny shore crabs, and in the multitude of small Crustacea that drift and swim in the sea, the chitin remains transparent, and the colours and patterns show through it as a framed picture through glass. In other Crustacea, especially large slow-moving kinds such as adult crabs and lobsters, the chitin of the young animal becomes increasingly impregnated at each moult with lime salts, until the well-known "shell" is produced. Naturally colour change can be seen only in types with a transparent exoskeleton.

HERMIT CRABS

One of the most simple and interesting examples of colour change was noticed by one of the writers at the Plymouth Laboratory, where two large kinds of hermit crabs (*Eupagurus bernhardus* and *E. prideauxi*), dredged up from moderately deep water, are always to be seen in the aquarium tanks.

Hermit crabs are known for their habit of living within empty sea-shells. If you picture a tiny lobster with no shell at all on the hind part of its body and this part twisted round like the tail end of a winkle, you will have some idea of a hermit crab. The crab trundles about with its shelly house on its back, or, as it were, sits in the door of this house and waits for food to come within reach. The crab must be wary, for fish are eager to snap at the exposed part of its body. Any quick movement causes the crab to pop right inside the shell, leaving nothing to be seen but hard, closely folded pincers that form a kind of stopper half-way up the shell. The two kinds of hermit crabs mentioned above are to some extent protected from attack by the fact that each has a big sea anemone on its shell, and sea anemones sting.

The tiny hermit crabs of rock pools, that can be found in almost any kind of empty winkle shell, have no anemone companions. To see one, wait quietly beside a shallow pool until you notice a snail shell moving with unnatural speed. Pick it up and you will see the crab's pincers almost out of sight round the bend of the shell. If you lay the shell in the pool, with the opening upwards, the crab will soon emerge, right itself and move away.

For observations on colour change, the hermit with the Cloaklet anemone on its shell proved the most suitable (*Eupagurus prideauxi* with *Adamsia palliata*). Left undisturbed in wide shallow bowls of sea water it comes partly out of its shell, exposing all the front part of its body, and even allowing a glimpse of its hind end to be seen. Only the legs, claws, and tip of the head are covered with hard shell; elsewhere the chitin is suffiicently transparent for skin colours to be seen clearly, especially on the soft concealed tail or abdomen.

When kept in bowls painted dull black inside, the hermits become a bright rosy pink. In white bowls they take on a pale grey-blue colour. The shade of pinkness or paleness depends, however, on the amount of light present. In dim light the animals in the black bowl are pale pink, in bright light they are bright pink. The animals in the white bowl are paler in dim light than in bright light. At night the crabs all become pale, regardless of their background. The results are summarised in the Table on p. 75.

Scattered over the hermit crab's skin are pigment cells or chromatophores containing red pigment, of a carotin type. If the pigment is contracted at the centre of the chromatophore it forms a speck almost invisible to the unaided eye. If the pigment is fully spread in the radiating branches of the chromatophore a definite red spot can be seen. Hence the pale or rosy colour of the skin. Other chromatophores, fewer in number, contain an opaque pigment, white or primrose yellow in colour. This contributes but slightly to the general colour effect, and is not included in the following account. Chemically, this pigment is an amino acid.

Colour change in Crustacea takes place in two distinct ways. In one the chromatophores are directly responsive to light. Light causes them to expand, the amount of expansion being roughly proportional to the strength of the light. In the absence of light they contract. This behaviour, being presumably of a simple and fundamental type, goes by the name of primary response or effect. The other way in which colour change takes place is less direct, and is known as the secondary response. When light strikes the animal's eyes, a stimulus passes to its nervous system, which causes the release of chemical substances or hormones into the blood; according to the stimulus and the hormone it evokes, the chromatophores expand or contract.

When hermit crabs are in darkness, neither pigment cells nor eyes receive the stimulus of ordinary light. The chromatophores are contracted and the animal appears pale. In daylight, if the animals are on a dark background, that is, one that absorbs light rays, the eyes are stimulated in a certain way and a hormone is released which causes the chromatophores to expand and the animal to deepen in colour. This hormone will be called for convenience B, that is, the hormone released for the black background response (Hogben's nomenclature). If the animals are on a pale background in daylight, that is a light-scattering background, the eyes are stimulated in a different way and a second hormone is released. This is hormone W, the hormone released for the white background response. The black and white backgrounds used in laboratory experiments are extreme cases of the light and dark backgrounds to which animals would need to adjust themselves under natural conditions.

The rosy colour of hermit crabs on black, and their pale colour on white, is in the main a secondary effect. But we saw that the quality of the pale or rosy colour varies according to the strength of the light. This is evidently due to primary and secondary effects working sometimes together and sometimes in opposition. So much for the colour change of the front part of the hermit's body. But what of the tail, tucked away inside the shell and receiving no light at the tip and very little near the shell entrance? Perhaps the chromatophores are absent or reduced through lack of use? Actually they are well developed and very sensitive, and their behaviour gives interesting additional evidence as to the behaviour of the chromatophores of the front part of the body.

When a hermit sits in its natural position, with its head and body (cephalothorax) outside the shell, and its tail (abdomen) inside, the head is in light and the tail in semi- or total darkness. Under these conditions the primary effect of light should be clearly seen. This is the case. Put a hermit under good light in a black bowl, so that its head end becomes bright pink. Remove it quickly from its shell, and the tail is found to be quite pale. But as you watch the tail flushes a delicate rose colour, and within ten minutes is as pink as the head. Both light and hormone stimulus cause the tail chromatophores to expand. While the tail was in darkness it received hormone B, together with the rest of the body, but this was not strong enough to compete successfully with the primary effect of light (actually, absence of light) which was dominant and forced the chromatophores to remain contracted.

To take one other example, if the crabs are on a white background in dim light, both the exposed and concealed chromatophores are found to be contracted. This is due to secondary effect in the main, with primary effect contributing. If the crabs are then moved to a bright light, the primary effect causes a partial expansion of the exposed chromatophores, while the concealed ones remain contracted.

So we may conclude that where the front part of the hermit crab is concerned, the direct effect of light can enhance the background adaptation brought about through the eyes, or it may diminish this, but not sufficiently to destroy its value. As regards the crab's tail end, the direct effect of light overrides the background response caused by hormones, but, as the tail is hidden, this makes no difference to the animal's background harmony. It seems not unreasonable to suppose that the concealed chromatophores are more sensitive to light than the exposed ones.

SHELL-LESS HERMITS

If hermits are removed from their shells, after a day or so background adaptation takes place uniformly all over the body. It is no easy matter to remove a hermit from its shell. It clings tightly inside by means of pincers on the tiny limbs of the tail end, and pulling damages the animal without getting it out. The shell must be cut open very carefully with a strong instrument such as bone forceps. It is impracticable to cut off the shell fast enough to be sure of observing the condition of the pigment cells before light affects them. So artificial shells were made which could be removed in a few seconds. Wide-mouthed glass tubes of very light weight were surrounded by bags of thick rubber sheeting and held in place on the crab by a detachable collar. The crabs could move about easily with these shells.

Various other Crustacea—for example, some species of squat-lobster (*Galathea strigosa* and *G. dispersa*)—are like the large hermit crab in having a simple chromatophore system of red and primrose-yellow pigments. Varying from pale pink on a light background to light red on a dark background, at night all become pale and translucent.

COLOUR CHANGE OF THE PRAWN

In the hermit crab each chromatophore contained one pigment only. This is true for some of the scattered pigment cells of the prawn, but the majority, and those responsible for the major effect of colour change, contain two pigments. In shrimps three or four pigments occur together. The prawn has small yellow chromatophores scattered over its general body surface and small red ones on its tail plates or uropods. Large chromatophores containing both red and yellow pigments are arranged in bands and clusters at various positions on the body and form a definite pattern. In symmetrical positions here and there are other large chromatophores containing the opaque white or primrose-yellow pigment together with a centre spot of red pigment. These will be referred to as white chromatophores. (Plates 11–12.)

NATURE OF COLOUR RESPONSE

Nature of stimulus		Environment of crabs.	Chromatophores of head.	Visible colour effect.	Chromatophores of tail.	Visible colour effect.
Secondary effect		Black background Bright light	Expansion	Bright pink	Slight expansion	Almost maximum pallor.
Primary effect		Bright light	Expansion		Contraction	
Secondary effect		Black background Dim light	Expansion	Paler pink	do.	do.
Primary effect		Dim light	Slight contraction			
Secondary effect		White background Bright light	Contraction	Very pale pink	Contraction	Maximum pallor
Primary effect		Bright light	Slight expansion		Contraction	
Secondary effect		White background Dim light	Contraction	Pale blue-grey	do.	do.
Primary effect		Dim light	Contraction			
		Darkness	do.	Maximum pallor	do.	do.

NATURE OF STIMULUS

Note.—It is convenient to refer to expansion and contraction of chromatophores. But in Crustacea the chromatophore itself does not move. It is surrounded by an elastic permeable membrane which does not change its shape but within it migration of pigment granules takes place by protoplasmic streamings. The rate of migration is affected by the osmotic pressure within the chromatophore, and the hormones may act by altering the permeability of the chromatophore membrane.

A living prawn is quite a beautiful object if examined closely. Through the transparent covering of chitin the muscles which compose so much of its body appear like slightly clouded glass, and on this background, in the transparent skin, are set the rows and dots of coloured pigment cells. Prawns found in a sandy pool or creek can hardly be seen until they move, so perfectly does their colour tone with the expanse of sand around them. A strong hand-lens reveals that the large chromatophores of the pattern bands have their red pigment concentrated into specks of colour, but their yellow pigment, and that of the yellow chromatophores of the general surface, is spread out to some extent. The pigment in the white chromatophores is fully spread, each making a conspicuous white spot. Thus on its semi-transparent body the prawn has white and pale yellow dots, with touches of black contributed by the eyes and by the dark pigment marking the course of the nerve-cord—just the effect to blend perfectly with the pale speckly sand.

If however, we take a net through dense clusters of dark weed hanging from boulders, or through a weed-carpeted rock pool, the prawns taken there show bright bands of colour on their legs and bodies and a general flush of red. They appear altogether more solid and colourful than the prawns from sandy ground. The red and yellow pigments are well spread out and the white chromatophores are less in evidence. (Plate 10.)

If some of these dark-coloured prawns are put in a large white bowl with sand on the bottom, and watched, quite a dramatic change sets in. A clear blue patch begins to surround each red-containing pigment cell, and within this blue patch the many-branched red rays shorten and thicken until all are collected in a central knot. The yellow pigment also withdraws, but not quite so fully as the red. The white chromatophores become conspicuous, and gradually the blue diffuses out more and more, and in from one and a half to two hours fades right away. The prawn is now in harmony with its sandy background. The nature and function of this transitory blue pigment which accompanies the contraction (and to a lesser extent the expansion) of the red chromatophores is not yet fully understood.

The prawn's adaptation from a dark to a light background begins with great rapidity. The blue pigment is obvious within one to two minutes. The main contraction of red and yellow pigments takes from twelve to fifteen minutes, and the effect seems complete in thirty to forty minutes after the transfer was made. Complete equilibrium with the background is, however, usually delayed until the following day. The reverse transfer, from a pale to a dark background, begins more slowly and takes longer to complete. There is a lapse of three or four minutes before the pigments show any sign of movement. The main expansion of red and yellow takes about twenty minutes, and good adaptation is achieved in from forty to sixty minutes. Final details of adjustment are complete by the next day. One thinks at first that background adjustment is over in an hour; but if a group of such prawns are put in a black bowl containing other prawns which have been there for forty-eight hours, the two groups can be distinguished at a glance.

The prawn's adjustments to background conditions result mainly from stimuli to the eyes, and are thus of the nature of a secondary response. The primary response to light is also strong, just as it is in the hermit crab. Prawns in a pale bowl cannot go completely colourless if they are in a bright light, but if their bowl is moved into shadow they complete their adaptation. So important is the primary effect that if observations on colour change are made in daylight, a record of the light intensity, which is much more variable than one would imagine, must be made at the same time by means of a photoelectric cell. An alternative is to work in a dark room with a source of artificial light which does not vary.

The primary response to light shows itself under these circumstances: prawns adapted to a white background in light and then transferred to darkness remain pale. If, in their white bowl, they are now brought into the light, all the pigments rapidly begin to expand until the animals are definitely pink. Soon, however, they pale again and achieve background harmony. Light caused quick expansion of all pigments, and not until the white background hormone W had been released into the circulation in sufficient amount (due to the secondary response through the eyes) could the red and yellow pigments be contracted and the effect of light overcome.

A useful check on the extent of the primary effect of light can be made by blindfolding the animals. A stiff mixture of lampblack and collodion painted over the eyes sets at once into a light-proof cap, which does no damage to the eyes and can easily be removed. Animals with covered eyes still show some spreading or withdrawal of pigments according to the intensity of light that they receive. It should be mentioned that in the prawn (*Leander serratus*) the white chromatophores are almost if not entirely free from hormone control, but extremely sensitive to light. In the brackish water prawn (*Palaemonetes varians*) it is probable that the white chromatophores are under hormone control, but from a different source from that of the hormones which regulate the red and yellow chromatophores.

The colour condition of animals in darkness has often proved something of a puzzle. Most animals whose chromatophores are under the control of hormones assume an intermediate condition, rather pale, in darkness. A very different condition is shown by prawns which have become adapted to a dark background in daylight, and remain on this background at the onset of darkness. In darkness they become definitely more red and achieve an expansion of red pigment never seen in the daytime. It would appear that darkness constitutes a stimulus of unique character. That this is the case seems borne out by the fact that animals adapted to a white background in light sometimes go partly or fully red if suddenly plunged into darkness.

This question of the action of darkness as a unique stimulus is one that deserves to be appreciated fully. It has already been mentioned that animals whose chromatophores are under hormone control pass into a pale phase in darkness, a condition almost intermediate in character. Darkness undoubtedly presents a condition or stimulus quite distinct from any experienced during daylight conditions. This appears to be true for the human subject. Professor F. Allen, who has done extensive work on colour vision in the human eye, states that when the retina of one eye is stimulated by light of a pure spectral hue (for example red) above a certain intensity, then the sensitivity of the other eye is enhanced for the colour sensations red, green and violet, and especially for whichever of these is the complementary to the stimulating colour. But if the light stimulus falls below a certain critical intensity, which for white light is about 0·25 metre-candles, the effect upon the retina is opposite in character—it inhibits or depresses the sensitivity for all three colour sensations. Thus vision in dim light becomes doubly difficult, partly because the light is weak, and partly because the dim light lowers retinal sensitivity. He adds that in certain conditions of illness the eyes are relieved of strain *in dim light rather than in darkness*. This fact is constantly put into practice in the sick-room by nurses and doctors.

No doubt we have all experienced the restful, neutral effect of twilight on the eyes. Darkness is very different—the eyes try to probe it, the darkness seems to impinge upon them. If we close the eyes and shut out the darkness, this slight sense of strain ceases. It may well be that in darkness such rays as are present have a strong effect. Being the only stimulus present, the eyes are particularly sensitive to them.   The fact that Professor Allen writes of colour vision does not prevent a comparison between the human eye and that of various animals.   Shrimps and prawns undoubtedly have a colour sense.

THE CONTROL OF COLOUR CHANGE BY HORMONES

It was through research on the brackish water prawn *Palaemonetes* that Perkins, working in America, discovered the hormone that contracts the chromatophores.   Although the phases of colour change had been fully studied some time before by various workers, there was no certainty as to how it took place..   The general opinion was that the chromatophores were controlled by the nervous system. Although the action of hormones was well known in Vertebrate animals, their presence in animals lower in the scale was only beginning to be discovered.

Perkins could find no evidence that the chromatophores of the prawn were under nervous control, but clear evidence that they are controlled by something circulating in the blood.   He devised a neat method of stopping the circulation to the tail end of the prawn and releasing it again at will, without damage to the animal.   He took a prawn with expanded chromatophores and stopped the main artery to the tail.   He then put the prawn on a white background, and found that the chromatophores of the front part of the body contracted, but those beyond the closed artery remained expanded.   When the artery was released, the chromatophores of the tail end also contracted.   Evidently a hormone was made in the front part of the body and distributed elsewhere by the blood circulation.   Perkins located the gland that makes this hormone in the stalk of the eye.   He was unable to discover a hormone which caused the chromatophores to expand.

Koller was working at the same time in Germany on the control of colour change in the shrimp, *Crangon*.   He searched for and located the gland responsible for making the hormone that causes the chromatophores to expand.   The gland making this hormone is just at the base of the spine projecting from the tip of the head in shrimps and prawns, and known as the rostral gland.   It is very easy to obtain and demonstrate the presence and action of the contracting hormone W.   The same cannot be said about the expanding hormone B.   Sometimes the rostral gland yields a substance which unmistakably brings about the dark background reaction.   More often it produces no result at all.   Evidently the whole story is not yet pieced together.

The problem was next approached by the method found so

successful by Prof. Hogben and his collaborators in the case of Vertebrates. This method is based on the time-graphs of the various phases of colour change. It was applied by H. G. Smith to the sand slater, *Ligia*, and shows beyond question that two hormones are concerned in the colour change of this animal. (Plate 9.) The method of demonstration of the two-hormone hypothesis, for *Ligia*, is given in Appendix III.

How the Eyes Regulate the Hormone Production

A study of the eyes of the sand slater shows clearly how the various stimuli of direct and reflected light evoke the hormones which ensure the correct colour response. It was already known that in certain animals with compound eyes the eye-units or ocelli are not all alike as regards their method of reception, and this helped to provide a clue.

The eyes of *Ligia* are not stalked, as are those of crabs and prawns, but lie close against the sides of the head. To take a homely illustration, they are like the halves of a haricot bean applied one each side of the head, with the rounded side of the bean outwards. By a series of experiments too long to describe here it was established that each eye consists of two areas having different functions. A dorsal area D receives light coming directly from above, and a latero-ventral area LV receives light coming from the sides and from below. On a black background the dorsal area D is stimulated by light, but the latero-ventral area LV receives no light stimulus, the light being absorbed by the dark background. On a white background the dorsal area D is stimulated by direct light, and at the same time the LV area is receiving light scattered by the pale background. Many variations can be played on this theme. But the physiological result is this: when D is stimulated there is an output of hormone B. When L plus V, or L or V alone, are stimulated, there is an output of hormone W.

We can now get a clearer view of the two-hormone mechanism for any phases of colour change. Consider the transference of pale animals to darkness. While on a white background all units of the eye are stimulated. Hormones B and W are both released, but W in sufficient excess to override B. When the animal is placed in darkness, all parts of the eye receive a new stimulus and the output of both B and W begins to be lowered, mutual adjustment being arrived at in the manner already considered.

The two-hormone mechanism has now been established for shrimps, since the date of Koller's work, and there is every probability that it also applies in the case of prawns. The ventral part of the eye is responsible for background adaptation, in prawns.

COLOUR CHANGE IN YOUNG SHORE CRABS

Shallow rock pools and the upper parts of the shore are the nursery of tiny shore crabs. These small creatures, from 2 to 4 centimetres across, show most varied colours and patterns. They may be sandy coloured or light green, or coloured much like a tabby cat. All show the usual colour changes in response to background and to darkness, but the pale and "tabby" kinds show the most conspicuous changes.

The chromatophores on the limbs of these animals can be watched very easily, for the chitin is quite transparent. Bands of melanophores are present and intermediate patches of white chromatophores. On the body, red pigment and melanin occur together in the same chromatophores, and white is abundant, especially over the gill regions.

These young individuals exhibit adaptation within thirty minutes. As the crabs age, this faculty is gradually lost, until when an inch and a half across they require a day or two to react. Darkly pigmented adult crabs show no change at all, though this can still be detected in pale yellow-green adults. The usual condition in adults is for all the chromatophores to be permanently expanded. Experiment shows that plenty of hormone B is produced by adult crabs, but little if any hormone W. This hormone W is almost certainly concerned in shrimps and their kindred with the deposition of calcium or lime in the shell. It is possible that the scarcity or absence of hormone W from the blood of adult crabs is connected with the heavy deposit of calcium in the thick shell.

It is certainly a matter of interest that hormone W should be found to have another function in addition to its work in regulating colour change. Perhaps hormone B will be found to have some other physiological property. It seems doubtful whether two hormones would be constantly present in the body without having some general physiological significance apart from their action on the chromatophores. The pituitary gland, which governs colour change in the lower Vertebrates, has manifold other functions.

ÆSOP'S OR CHAMELEON PRAWN, HIPPOLYTE

The colour phases of the tiny Chameleon prawn are more obvious than those of the common prawn, and appear under rather different circumstances.

This little prawn, never more than an inch in length, is fairly common in rock pools, but so difficult to detect that it is seldom discovered. This is partly because it tones perfectly with the sea-weed on which it lives, and partly because it clings motionless to the weed during the daylight hours. The best way to find it is to take a net repeatedly through bunches of weed in the pools, and turn the contents of the net carefully into a shallow dish. Sometimes vigorous shaking of a bunch of weed in a dish of sea water will dislodge the prawns.

On green weed *Hippolyte* is green, and on the various shades of brown and red weed it is again the exact colour of its setting. But supposing a prawn gets shaken from its moorings and carried away. It is only a feeble swimmer, and may not be able to find weed of just the right colour on which it can shelter. In that case the prawn assumes as soon as possible the colour of its new home, a process which is completed within a week. Usually these prawns are of one colour all over, and size, shape and posture make them appear just like a branch of the weed to which they cling. This is an example of special resemblance to a definite object, rather than the general resemblance shown by the common prawn to a large-scale background effect.

The chameleon prawn manages all its colour effects with red, yellow and blue pigments. On green weed it displays the yellow and blue, concealing the red. Other colours are produced by other suitable arrangements. Each chromatophore contains all three pigments.

The young chameleon prawn spends the first weeks of its life drifting in the surface waters off the coast. It gets carried inshore as a tiny transparent creature, and settles on the first weed that chance presents. Chromatophores soon appear, and the prawn takes on the colour of its home.

These little creatures, so still and solid-looking in the daytime, undergo a fairy-like transformation during the hours of darkness. Their bodies become a delicate translucent blue and they dart here and there, feeding on fine seaweed and on the minute animal life to be found amongst it. It is an unforgettable experience to bring a company of these tiny water sprites from a dark room into a circle of light, and for a few seconds to admire their charming appearance. Then, like the old tale of the fairy gold that turned suddenly to a handful of dead leaves, they become drab and dull— the blue gives place to the former sober shades.

Colour Change in Cuttlefish and their Relatives

Perhaps the most wonderful of colour displays are given by those strange creatures the cuttlefish, octopus, squid and devil-fish (Mollusca: Class Cephalopoda).

The octopus lives concealed in crevices amongst rocks, or swims close to the rocky floor. It may range in colour from a dull crimson hue to a grisly grey, merging well with its surroundings. The octopus feeds mainly on crabs. It keeps a sharp look-out from its crevice and, when a crab comes near enough, darts out its strong arms, studded with suckers, and seizes its prey. An octopus is often hauled up in a crab-pot which it has entered to eat the captive crabs.

The cuttlefish, an active swimmer, keeps close to the sea bottom, and may conceal itself in the sand. It may dart out after its prey or, remaining in position, uncurl from two pockets a pair of long tentacles which effect the capture.

The squid is a swift-moving creature with a long tapering body. It lives mainly in the surface waters, feeding on fish, and numbers of squid are often met with pursuing shoals of fish. Tiny kinds of cuttlefish with pearly-white bodies also live in the surface waters.

Colour in the animal world is no respecter of persons. These uncanny-looking creatures, with their large round eyes, parrot-like beaks and sinister tentacles, can hold an observer fascinated by their subtle, beautiful colour displays. I once saw a little cuttlefish just brought up by the net and lying on the deck of a trawler. Over a skin like alabaster spread rhythmic waves of rosy colour. These faded away, but for a while points of colour, like tiny flashing jewels of red and gold, came and went. Then the display was over, for the animal was dead. Small squids are sometimes kept in aquarium tanks. Here a shoal can be watched swimming to and fro. Delicate waves of golden-orange colour and warm red tints shimmer across the skin, like blushes coming and going. Devil-fish, though varying only from ashen-grey to black, show an endless variety of subtle tints.

Colour Mechanism

Each pigment, whether red, yellow, brown or black, is held in a tiny sphere whose size is increased or decreased by radiating groups of muscle fibres each having its own nerve supply. A black pigment sphere, for example, when at its smallest is just visible as a grey speck, while at its biggest it looks like a tiny black pinhead. It takes two-thirds of a second to change one way or the other. So a devil-fish, with lightning speed, can pass from palest grey to black, the black spheres almost touching when at their darkest. The play of colour is controlled by the highly developed nervous system, acting on impressions received through the eyes.

ACTION AND COLOUR

All these agile and predatory creatures are equipped with excellent powers of vision; indeed, their eyes are as well formed as our own. And they are well armed with beak and suckers. But their bodies are soft and good to eat, and fish and other strong swimmers take any chance of capturing them. The colour displays occur when they are excited either by being disturbed or chased or by the sight and pursuit of their own food. An octopus, clinging bat-like in its rocky niche, can hardly be made out in the moderate light of an aquarium tank, its greyish-brown shades mingling with the rocky walls. But if the glass just in front of it is tapped vigorously, waves of deep crimson colour pass over its body. It begins to writhe its tentacles and raise and lower its body, for all the world like a dark-red demon of the rocks. It may also become suffused with colour at the sight of food, owing to the fact that its mouth "begins to water". When cuttlefish eat they deepen in colour, for while their salivary glands are active an adrenalin-like hormone is released which acts on certain nerve junctions concerned with colour change.

These "blushes" are entirely due to skin pigments and are not caused by red blood rushing to the surface, as in the human subject. The cuttlefish's blood is almost colourless or very pale blue.

These displays of colour seem hardly of advantage to the animal in capturing its food. At first sight their effect would seem to be to reveal its whereabouts. Yet when a cuttlefish hunts a crab it needs to manœuvre into a suitable position to make the capture. Meanwhile waves of colour pass over its body, giving a rippling effect, and this may serve to distract the crab's attention until the moment comes to strike. When it is the cuttlefish's turn to be hunted, how baffling it must be to the hunter when its prey hardly looks the same for two seconds at a time. When a cuttlefish is thoroughly disturbed two large black spots appear on its back, staring out from a surface of gleaming white. The black "pupils" dilate, and a black crescent appearing beneath each makes the effect still more startling. Meanwhile the edges of the fins become outlined in black. Then with a lightning change the "pupils" disappear and long black stripes stand out along the back, only to flicker and disappear. From black eyes on white, zebra pattern, and all-black, the quick-change performance plays to and fro. A hunter is much more likely to sheer off than to risk a snap at such an unknown quantity. (Plate 5.)

Whatever their survival value or assistance in food getting, these sensitive and varied plays of colour always accompany and express some state of excitement. The well-developed nervous system and senses of these creatures accord with these colourful surface signals of their transient moods. When they are at rest their colours are neutral, they attract no attention. When roused, a display of varying intensity results, on which alternative interpretations can be put. Perhaps the display is just a form of self-expression. It can seem to have no other explanation in the squids and tiny cuttles of the surface waters, where every deepening of colour serves only to make its owner more conspicuous either to enemies or to prey.

When *in extremis* cuttlefish and squid can play a trump card. They carry with them a sac filled with dark sepia pigment. The instant this is discharged the water around becomes an inky black and capture is impossible.

CHAPTER VII

CHAMELEON AND FROG

THE chameleon is a variety of lizard, found in various parts of the African continent. It lives in trees and bushes, and can sometimes be found on hedges and plants in gardens. Chameleons are described by Aristotle (384–322 B.C.), and through subsequent centuries travellers in North Africa have continued to be intrigued by this strange-looking animal and its rapid colour phases. The chameleon's behaviour became proverbial, and it was finally credited with achievements quite beyond its considerable natural capacity.

The chameleon has a quaint appearance. (Plate 7.) Its head seems covered by a stiff helmet jutting out at the back. Perhaps this is what suggested its name, which means " dwarf lion ". Fancy may have traced a likeness to a lion's mane, especially when the lizard was tawny brown in colour. Great round eyes protrude from deep sockets on either side of the head. It has a horny suit, looking rather like fine chain mail, finished off with a jimped effect down the back. Moving and resting as it does for the greater part of its life amongst stems and branches, the chameleon has very peculiar feet well suited to grasping this type of support. The toes are divided into two groups, so that the animal has a kind of cloven foot which grasps the branch like a pair of flexible pliers. Its long tapering tail winds round a branch and makes an effective anchor. For much of its time the chameleon is motionless. Its main food consists of insects, which are often caught unawares in a startling manner. Neither colour nor movement betrays the chameleon; when an insect comes within a few inches, out shoots a long slender tongue with an expanded sticky tip and the insect is trapped. When a chameleon moves it is with very slow deliberate placing of one foot at a time, like a study in slow motion. It can stalk and capture food by means of these stealthy movements, and they have another advantage, for by such slow motion the chameleon has a chance of escaping the notice of enemies. Many birds, snakes and lizards find chameleons palatable food, and they are rather helpless creatures. Although their skin has a horny thickening in the form of bosses it affords little protection against sharp beaks and teeth. The chameleon's main chance of safety lies in concealment, and both immobility and colour harmony with the leafy setting contribute to this result.

A kind of chameleon common in Kenya has yet another possible means of escape. The hornbill is one of its chief enemies, and a writer describes how, when walking under trees while this bird is about, numerous small thuds may be heard as chameleons fall to the ground to avoid being eaten.

A chameleon may display a most varied livery during the twenty-four hours. At night it is pale fawn with yellow patches; at dusk and dawn it passes through a darker phase of greyish-green; during the daylight hours it assumes shades of green according to its setting, with spots and patches of black and pale brown. When excited, orange spots and maroon patches are displayed. If it rests on a branch in the bright sunshine its body is very dark, but where a shadow falls upon it, the skin is paler. A dark chameleon placed among bright green leaves will become green in about fifteen minutes.

The dwarf chameleon of the Cape (*Lophosaura pumila*) may be taken as an example of the colour behaviour of chameleons in general. At its darkest it becomes black all over. At its palest it is vivid yellow-green with pale fawn and grey markings. These markings belong to a fixed pattern on the sides of the body, made by patches and lines of colour. So the colour changes concern partly the general body and partly the patterned areas of the sides. In the darkest condition the brown-black melanin pigment eclipses all others both on the body and on the sides.

The body colour ranges from black through dark, medium and pale green to primrose-yellow. The patterned area is very colourful. In an intermediate condition it is outlined in bright blue, its central part ranges from orange to brown and has inlet patches of dark blue or grey. In this condition the pattern is set on a body colour of green. In its pale condition the patterned area is outlined in pale grey or blue, with centre of pale fawn and the inlet patches pale grey, all displayed on a body colour of yellow-green. Such changes are certainly enough to arouse astonishment and curiosity in anyone who sees them.

In picturing dwarf chameleons in their natural setting we must think of them in hedges, and in various bushes and trees, such as the Cassia and Eucalyptus, with its cinnamon-brown trunk and grey-green foliage. The chameleon can take on almost any green tone of grass and leaves. Sometimes it rests on the pale yellow-green bracts of flower-heads, and then it takes on a primrose-yellow colour, its lightest and most vivid tint. Often the foliage is brilliantly lit and there are deep black shadows between the leaves. It is in strong light only that the chameleon becomes black. We can also picture brown and grey-brown branches, dark when in shadow, light fawn or silver-grey where the light strikes full upon them. There are shadows of blue or purple tones, complementary to the green of living and the yellow of dead leaves. Here and there are gnarled effects and irregular patches of bark and broken ends of twigs.

The chameleon's angular head, jimped back, bent limbs and colour scheme all help it to blend with such a setting. The general skin colour tones with the position it occupies at the moment, and the patterned area serves to break the outline, suggesting irregular shadow, or a scar or patch of rough bark. If the animal has one side exposed to the sun and the other side in shadow, the side exposed to the sun is darker in colour, with the result that it does not appear as a solid object cast into relief by light. It takes about four minutes for a chameleon to pass from a pale to a dark condition.

How the Colour Changes are Produced

The chameleon's outfit for colour effects consists of four distinct layers in the skin.

At the base of the skin, or embedded in the next layer above, are pigment cells containing black-brown melanin, known as melanophores. Next comes a layer which appears white * by reflected light and supplies a background against which the colours

* Owing to guanin crystals.

of the upper layers are well displayed. Above the white layer comes a zone which appears blue by reflected light, again an optical or structural effect. The upper layer is of yellow pigment. Now the stage is set; to understand the performance two further facts must be known. First, the yellow pigment can to some extent spread out to make a continuous layer, or can aggregate so that light passes down into the layers beneath. Second, the melanin may be withdrawn out of sight within the cell bodies at the base of the skin, or may migrate to various levels up hollow branches passing to the surface, or spread as a dense network over the surface, concealing all beneath it. The various pigment groupings that give the range of body colours are listed below.

Colour effect.	How produced.
Yellow.	Melanin concealed below; yellow fully spread at surface.
Pale green.	Yellow partly withdrawn, blue layer exposed to light.
Medium green.	As for pale green, but melanin ascends some way up the melanophore branches, giving a darker tone.
Dark green.	Melanin ascends to the surface and spreads out slightly there.
Black.	Melanin forms a dense network over the surface, obscuring green.

As regards the colours of the patterned area: in the margin the colours range through grey, blue and dark blue to black. There are present the layer of melanophores, the white layer and the blue layer.

Grey.	Presumably the melanin spreads over the white layer, so that light passing through the blue layer is absorbed and not reflected.
Blue.	The blue layer showing to full advantage over the white layer.
Dark blue.	Melanin spread some distance up its channels in the blue layer, deepening its tone.
Black.	Melanin concealing blue.

The colour band within the margin changes from pale fawn through orange to brown. Here a layer of orange pigment cells rests on the white and melanin zones.

Pale fawn.	Orange pigment concentrated to centre of its cells. Melanin contracted.
Orange.	Orange pigment fully diffused.
Brown.	Melanin spread up through the diffused orange.
Black.	Melanin concealing orange.

In individual chameleons little bumps or tubercles of orange occur in rows in the general body area. They pass through the same colour range as just described. The changing of the inlet patches from pale grey or fawn through dark blue or grey to black need not be separately described.

The dwarf chameleon of the Cape gives birth to living young ones, several in a litter. At birth they are grey in colour and about 4½ cm. long. Their colour tone ranges from black to almost pure white, and only when they are almost full grown do they develop the bright colours typical of the adult chameleon.

MECHANISM OF THE COLOUR CHANGES

Sense cells in the skin and in the retina of the eye are stimulated by direct light, and by light reflected from the surroundings. These stimuli pass to the brain, and thence along nerve fibres of the sympathetic nervous system to the pigment cells. The whole colour range is of the nature of unconscious reflex action. Fuller details are given in the Reptile section of Chapter X.

THE CHAMELEON CALLS A BLUFF

There is one chameleon (*C. dilepis*) that does not rely on passive concealment for safety. In the presence of danger it distends its lungs with air so that its body appears blown up like a balloon. It becomes pitch black, opens its jaws to display the bright yellow lining to its mouth, and raises scaly flaps at the back of its head. To give the full benefit of this formidable display, the chameleon tilts its body so that the broadest view is towards the enemy. It hisses like a snake. Cott observed this device to be highly successful against an over-curious dog.

So the colour response made seems to vary with circumstance and with the creature's moods. Sometimes it becomes very conspicuous, as though in warning, at other times it makes itself appear smaller and slighter, and colour harmony completes the self-effacement.

THE FROG, A LIVING WEATHER-GLASS

There is some truth in the country saying that you can tell, by looking at the colour of frogs, what kind of weather to expect for the next few hours. Frogs change their colour to a remarkable extent, partly according to the appearance of their surroundings, and partly according to the temperature and dryness or humidity of the air.

If we are used to the appearance of frogs we can make a fair guess, by looking at one, as to the kind of place and conditions it has just come from. Here is a case in point. Two naturalists met by chance in a country lane. One found the other looking at something he held in his hands, and was asked, "Where do you think I found this frog a moment ago?" The frog was very dark all over, brown-black with an olive tinge. "You must have found it in some cold damp place, on dark stones or earth," was the reply. "Yes. I went to look at that old well built into the thickness of the wall, and the frog was in a niche amongst the cold dark stones."

The frog was put on the ground. It hopped a short distance and half buried itself in a tussock of long grass. The day was sunny and warm. The friends kept still and glanced at the frog from time to time as they chatted, leaning on a gate. Soon its body was an olive green on which dark stripes and flecks formed a broken pattern. Some of the dark stripes continued from the body straight down across the folded hind limbs, obscuring the junction between limb and body. A dark band along each side of the head diverted attention from the bright and prominent eyes. Still the frog remained motionless, steadily becoming more difficult to distinguish from the grass. A quarter of an hour had gone by. "Give it another fifteen minutes and it will be safe." And so it was. The frog was now the green of the grass tussock and its dark lines and flecks looked like the shadow patches amongst the grass. The bright light, warm dry air and grassy surroundings had, as it were, made deep impressions on the animal's perception and on the mysterious mechanism of nerve and gland, and expressed themselves outwardly upon its skin. Inwardly, the rate of its breathing and heart-beat were quickened; its muscles could move more freely. Very likely it would feel hungry and both ready and able to catch a fly. How different from its cold, sluggish state beside the well, with all its faculties slowed down.

Frogs and toads are creatures that wander considerable distances and over backgrounds so diverse as grassy meadow, dark soil trampled bare by cattle around a pond, grey stones, or the russet carpet of a woodland. With such natural settings they quickly become harmonised in tone and colour. Toads may take up residence in a garden for several years. A lady who had a scenic garden with rockeries, and a stream running through, thought she had three toads in the garden, a speckled brown toad living in a niche among the rockery stones, a mottled green toad living among the rhododendrons and an olive-black toad on the mud by the stream. Only as these toads became friendly towards her and she found they all had a certain mannerism in common, did she begin to suspect that they were one and the same toad, as proved to be the case.

Even if a frog or toad lives for a whole season in, for example, the same meadow, it needs to adjust its colour continually. It must harmonise with the silver-grey of the grass at dawn, with its green colour and varying lights and shadows during the daytime, for it is in danger from enemies every hour of the day. This harmony with the appearance of the environment is effected through the eyes. Temperature and moisture conditions are, however, registered by the skin; they also result in changes of colour. Sometimes impressions received through the eyes are reinforced by those received by the skin; at other times the two sets of stimuli work in opposite directions.

Dry weather tends to make frogs paler in colour, and wet weather deepens their tone. As damp earth is darker than dry earth and grey skies and moist air intensify the colours of vegetation, so in the case of a frog amongst grass and mud around a pond, eyes and skin-sense both tend to make the animal dark. During a dry period the same locality would take on a lighter tone, and so would the frog.* But if a frog found itself in a sunken garden paved with light-coloured stone, in damp weather, the stimulus received by its eyes would evoke the response of a very light skin colour, but the stimulus received by its skin would modify this.

Warm temperatures tend to make a frog pale, and cold temperatures the reverse. This may be an advantage in that an expanse of dark melanin can absorb any available heat. A frog is at its darkest on a dark-coloured background in cold, damp conditions, as amongst the cold dark stones by the well. It is at its palest in warm dry conditions on a light-coloured background, for example amongst young meadow grass on a warm bright day in spring. The temperature factor may, like that of moisture, work with or against the other factors making for colour change. A table is given in Appendix IV showing which factors tend to override others, when acting in opposition.

It is evident that the frog's skin colour at any given time is a mirror of its environment, a complete algebraic summary of its surroundings—the colour of the earth it rests on and the plants that surround it, the condition of the air, dry or moist, warm or cold, that surrounds its body, the quality and intensity of the light that enters its eyes and illuminates its skin. The creature is in complete harmony with nature. Its living matter responds to the natural forces that play upon it and through it. The obvious

---

* In contrast to earth and vegetation, which themselves undergo no change, the frog achieves its toning by internal changes manifest on its skin.

result—the external colour harmony between the frog and its surroundings—is a useful contribution to the frog's well-being. It is the result of inner adjustments of nerve, brain and gland. But it is an outer sign of great significance, in that it shows how intimately the whole creature, not only its skin, responds to the natural forces which govern its life.

THE FROG'S PIGMENTS

The frog's range of colours results from the interplay of three pigments: melanin, which is pale brown when thinly spread and black when very dense, a yellow or orange-yellow pigment, and an opaque white. Each speck of pigment is contained separately in a pigment cell or chromatophore. The chromatophore is something like a star with irregularly branched rays. The rays remain extended, and within them the pigment disperses or collects according to circumstance. If it collects at the centre, the pigment appears as a speck. If it disperses fully in the branches, it makes a coloured spot. The branches of the melanin cells (melanophores) often interlace, producing a dense network. The yellow pigment collects or disperses, but the white pigment is immovable.

In addition to movable chromatophores over the whole body surface, the frog has a permanent pattern of dark stripes and patches on its upper surface and pale areas on its underside. In the frog's palest condition the pattern almost fades away; in the darkest condition the pattern itself becomes so dark (for it has many movable melanophores) that it is again obscured. But in intermediate conditions it is well in evidence, and plays an important part in breaking up what would otherwise be too large an area of the same colour. It is this pattern that contributes the stripes and flecks that suggest shadows, as in the case of the frog sheltering in the tussock of grass.

The frog's skin is thin, soft and almost transparent. Nearest the outside lie the yellow pigment cells, and beneath them the white. The melanophores lie partly among the yellow cells and partly among and below the white. For pale colour effects the melanin withdraws, exposing the yellow and white pigments. For dark effects the melanin makes a dense network and the diffused yellow adds to the opaque appearance of the skin; the white is hidden. Green is not due to a pigment, but is an optical effect. Except when the skin is in its darkest phase, light penetrates through it to the white layer, which acts as a reflector for blue-green wave lengths.* It is these waves passing upwards through the yellow

* Melanin in a certain stage of dispersion also scatters blue-green wave-lengths.

layer that give the appearance of green. The relative shades of yellow, green or brown visible at any time depend on the amount of light reaching the skin and on the mutual adjustment of yellow and brown pigments.

THE FROG'S RECEIVING AND TRANSMITTING SYSTEM

The frog has two distinct " receiving sets " with which it " picks up " the various conditions of its surroundings: these are the eyes and the skin. The eyes receive light direct from the sky and distinguish between bright and dim light and darkness. They also " see " the surroundings by receiving light reflected from objects within their field of vision. The train of events which leads from seeing a dark or a light background to effecting a suitable colour adjustment is as follows.

The retina of the eye is shaped like a shallow bowl, laid on its side. It may be thought of as divided into two areas. One area receives light-waves coming directly from the sky: this area is the back and lower part of the retina. The other area receives light-waves reflected from the background into the eye; this area consists of the peripheral parts of the retina. In the nature of things, reflected light will also stimulate area one, but direct light can never stimulate area two. When the frog is on a black background which reflects no light, then only the first area is stimulated—area B for black. When it is on a white background, light is reflected on to the second area—area W for white.

Nerve fibres pass from the retina to the brain, and from the brain to the pituitary gland. When area B is stimulated by light, nerve impulses pass from it to the brain and thence to a part of the pituitary gland, which releases a special chemical substance or hormone into the blood-stream. The blood carries the hormone to the skin, where it causes the melanin and yellow pigments to spread out, resulting in a dark-coloured frog. When area W is stimulated, nerve impulses pass from it to the brain, and thence to another part of the pituitary gland. This produces a hormone which causes pigment to withdraw to the centre of the pigment cells and a pale-coloured frog results. It is inevitable that the " black " hormone is produced at the same time as the white, but its effect is overridden by that of the white.

If we wish to observe the adaptation of a frog to, for example, a green background, it is clear that to obtain a good result the " background " must extend up to or above its eye level. Only under these conditions will the maximum amount of reflected light reach area W of the retina. Thus a suitable green background can be provided by lining a small deep bowl with green moss.

The frog's second receiving set, its skin, has a remarkable range of reception. Under the base of the skin are nerve endings which are receptors for pain, pressure, and the texture of things with which the skin comes into contact. Other nerve endings register cold and heat. The frog also has receptors for moisture—a matter of life and death where this animal is concerned. Although it has lungs it draws much of its oxygen direct from the air into the blood-stream, through the moist skin. The skin is kept moist in the same way as our own nostrils, but in very dry air the moisture is lost faster than it can be produced. If the skin dries, the animal suffocates—hence the need for constant awareness of the state of the air, leading it to move to damp places and avoid dry ones.

Stimuli of temperature and moisture received by the skin are carried to the brain by nerves. In the brain, messages received from skin and eyes are, as it were, reviewed, and the extent of production of one or other of the hormones from the pituitary determined.

DIRECT ACTION OF LIGHT ON THE PIGMENTS

The pigments are not completely under the control of the brain and its agents the hormones, for they are directly responsive to light. When any but the most feeble light falls on the skin a slight spreading of pigment results. If two frogs are kept for half an hour or so under just the same conditions—for instance in two white basins with the same air temperature and the same amount of moisture in the bottom of the bowl—and then one basin is put in a dim and the other in a bright light, the frog in the bright light will be found to be the darker of the two. Of course frogs, like other animals, show individual differences, so for any such experiment two frogs as similar in colour as possible should be chosen.

COLOUR CHANGE IN TADPOLES

Tadpoles show very clear adjustment to background. Place some in a white bowl and some in a dark bowl, such as a green bulb bowl, on whose floor is dark mud or old black leaves from the pond bottom. After an hour transfer the tadpoles from the dark bowl into the pie dish. The contrast between the two sets of tadpoles is very striking. In tadpoles kept for a day or more in a white dish, the skin pigments contract to such a degree that with a good lens the skull and many other internal organs can be seen.

White and black backgrounds rarely occur in nature. It is

onvenient to use them in experiments merely because they give
he maximum effect which would be produced by natural pale
nd dark backgrounds.

CHAPTER VIII

CAMOUFLAGE AND ITS CONTRIBUTION TO SURVIVAL

DURING the second half of the nineteenth century the subject of
nimal camouflage came to the fore in the scientific world, and a
pecial terminology was adopted to describe the facts observed.
Darwin's conception of adaptation to environment and favourable
ariations resulting in survival of the fittest strongly coloured the
iewpoint on the whole question, with the result that every aspect
f animal camouflage had ascribed to it a utilitarian motive. Thus
eneral cryptic resemblance was termed " Protective Coloration ":
aunting colours which rendered animals conspicuous were des-
ribed as " Warning Coloration ". Strong resemblance between
wo living creatures of quite different type was termed " Mimicry ".
Every animal was supposed to have a better chance of survival as
result of its coloration, including the other aspects of camouflage
—form, posture and so on.

These terms are still in use, but their significance has been ex-
ended or modified as the result of further work and thought.
Warning coloration is now known by the alternative epithet of
" aposematic ", meaning " signalling away from ", in the sense
f " Keep off ". A moment's thought shows that " protective
oloration " can be used only in a strictly limited sense. The
nimal life of a desert nearly all harmonises with the desert hues;
white is the livery worn in snow-clad regions, and green the general
olour of dwellers in the trees. In every geographical region where
certain colour scheme predominates, whether land or sea, the
najority of the fauna are found to harmonise with the prevailing
onditions: harmless plant feeders and those that prey upon them
re coloured alike. The necessary distinction is now made by
lescribing the harmless forms as showing " protective " and the
redatory forms " aggressive " resemblance. Camouflage helps the
ormer to survive by escaping detection, and the latter to survive
ly hunting more successfully.

Warning colour schemes are very distinctive. Where land
nimals are concerned, they consist of black combined with red,

orange or yellow, or black combined with white. Examples are the black and yellow of wasp and hornet, and of the cinnabar caterpillar so common on ragwort and groundsel; the red with black spots of the ladybird beetle, and the black and white of skunk and porcupine. Wasp and hornet are dangerous on account of their sting. Ladybirds are harmless, but can give out a pungent fluid which makes them very distasteful to any animal that tries to eat them. It is stated that trout are never seen to take the mayfly of vivid yellow colour, called by fishermen the Yellow May Dun. It is presumably unpalatable to them. Among poison-producing Amphibia with warning colours are the fire-bellied toad and the black-and-yellow fire salamander. The skunk, with its warning livery of black and white, is a formidable enemy if attacked. It lifts its large and conspicuous white tail, then shoots an evil-smelling fluid with the utmost precision right in the face of the misguided aggressor. The stench is so unbearable that a dog becomes sick and quite incapable of further hostilities.

These dangerous or distasteful creatures with their "red-flag" or "skull-and-crossbones" type of colouring are for the most part left severely alone. But there are also edible and harmless forms coloured in the same manner. These are described as showing "false warning colours". In many instances such animals closely resemble really dangerous and distasteful ones, which they are said to mimic. (See Chap. V.)

We may well enquire to what extent these various types of coloration actually affect the survival of the animals concerned. In the first place, protective camouflage (cryptic resemblance and false warning colours) can assist only against animals that hunt by sight. It can do little or nothing where those that hunt by touch or by smell are concerned. The point is well illustrated by reference to an extensive and varied group such as the spiders.

The jumping spiders (Salticidae) and other wandering varieties are comparatively long-sighted and see fairly clearly. They certainly hunt partly by sight. The Salticus spider itself can spring a distance of from one to two inches to make a capture, which implies clear focus within that range. But the majority of spiders (e.g. Argyopids) have eyes of little value as regards food capture. Touch and smell comprise their main sensory outfit. They measure size and apprise texture by contact, using their palps and tarsi or "feet". The palps and tarsi "smell" and feel at the same time. But since "smell"—which is very keen—involves close contact with the object, it has perhaps rather the nature of taste. The term "chemo-tactic sense" is best used to describe the spider's percep-

H. B. Cott

Plate 1   Bush Buck, Portuguese East Africa

Plate 2   Young Woodcock, newly hatched, on the floor of a wood

Plate 3   A South African Toad (*Bufo superciliaris*)

D. P. Wilson

Plate 4   Sea Hares (*Aplysia punctata*)

Plate 5   Cuttlefish, showing the " zebra " pattern

D. P. Wilson

Plate 6

Diagrams illustrating disruptive pattern

In the left-hand picture of each series, the shape of the animal can be clearly seen, and its tone contrasts with that of the background. In the central pictures a disruptive pattern in white, black, or black and white, is added. In each case the tone of the pattern gives the maximum contrast with that of the background. In the right-hand pictures the natural scenery of the background is included. This completes the camouflage effect, namely, the distraction of the eye of the observer from the form of the animal.

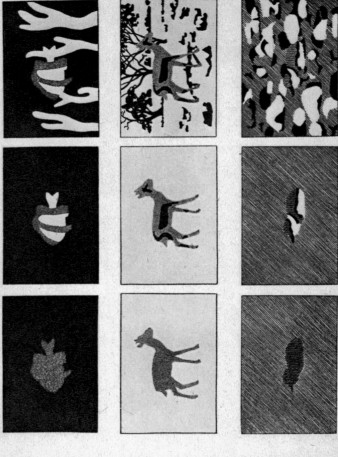

H. B. Cott

Plate 7
Spurred Chameleon

Plate 8 Angler Fish
(*Lophius piscatorius*)

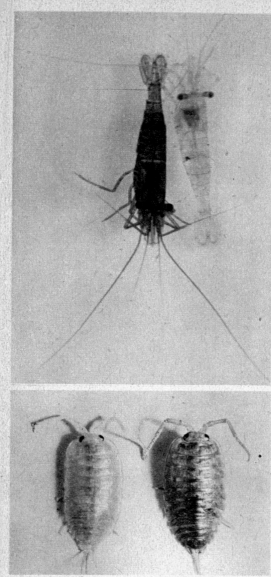

H. G. Smith

Dorothy Gibb

Plate 9 Sand Slaters (*Ligia oceanica*)

Plate 10 Prawns (*Leander serratus*)

One from a dark and one from a pale background

Plates 11 and 12

Chromatophores of the prawn (*Leander serratus*)

Some of the large red chromatophores of a pattern band are shown half expanded, with their yellow branches on either side. Two of the small red chromatophores, scattered over the general surface, are contracted and appear as yellow dots. Animal partly adapted to a dark background.

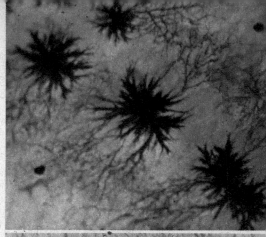

A single white chromatophore, fully expanded, and a few of the small red chromatophores of the general surface fully contracted. Animal adapted to a pale background.

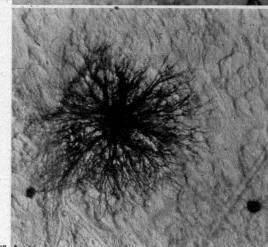

Russel B. Vernon

Plate 13

Natural colour changes in the Spur Dogfish (*Acanthias vulgaris* = *Squalis acanthias*)

H. Waring, by courtesy of the Royal Society

tion by smell-taste-touch. Protective colour schemes cannot save the prey of such spiders, and, moreover, they hunt mainly at night.

Even to the clear-sighted jumping spider, colour seems to have no significance. It attacks scarlet mites, and black-and-orange hover-flies, saw-flies and spiders. Equally it attacks " protectively " coloured brown Springtails (*Podura*) on brown earth and green Jassids on green leaves, so that neither protective nor warning colours avail. Where web-spinning spiders are concerned, camouflage of the spider's prey is again without significance, for the web catches all and sundry. The web-owner makes its selection according to the palatability and safety of the catch.

Spiders select or reject prey mainly on the ground of flavour. Many spiders have a very sensitive palate. Bristowe describes how they show discomfort after biting a distasteful insect—the mouth waters, and they wipe it repeatedly against a leaf or other nearby object. Ants, greenfly (aphids of all kinds), woodlice and some beetles all taste unpleasant to spiders. Earwigs are avoided, since they emit an unpleasant odour, and if attacked take up a menacing attitude with tail curled upwards. Any small insect which " mimics " the foregoing types is safe from attack by spiders, as for instance the edible Membracid bug and spider, which both mimic the leaf-cutting ant. It is worth noting, in passing, that spiders are invaluable in keeping down the numbers of craneflies and of certain other plant pests. Bristowe gives, as a conservative estimate, 50,000 spiders to the acre in England and Wales, a controlling army of considerable value.

We conclude, then, that camouflage is of no significance as a protection *against* spiders. Very many spiders are themselves camouflaged, however, and by this means obtain a measure of security against birds, reptiles and amphibia, all of which hunt by sight. Spiders show the usual counter-shading, and one kind (fam. Linyphiae), which stand upside down beneath their hammock webs, show reversed counter-shading with pale back and dark underside. Methods of camouflage used on the web itself are described in Chapter V. Spiders are used very extensively as food by other animals. They form a normal part of the diet of small insectivorous birds such as the robin, and are devoured in large numbers by starlings. They are a great source of food for bird nestlings, and are much eaten by toads, and to a lesser extent by frogs. Lizards and shrews account for many more. Great numbers of spiders' eggs are eaten by earwigs and woodlice.

Probably most people think of spiders as dull-coloured creatures, grey, black and mottled brown. Many, however, are of the colour of leaves and flowers, as for instance a kind with bright green abdomen marked by two light yellow stripes, blending with the terminal clusters of young needles of the cedar, among which it lives. While all such kinds of resemblance have protective value, they are at the same time an aid in aggression. A case in point is the yellow flower spider (*Misumena*). W. S. Bristowe devised an experiment to discover to what extent the spider's colour harmony with its background of dandelion flowers assisted in the capture of food. He placed sixteen dandelion flowers each one foot from its neighbour so as to form a large square. In the centre of eight alternate flowers he placed a small black pebble, and in the others a small dandelion-yellow pebble, all pebbles being the same size as the spider's body. He counted the insects which visited each flower in the course of half an hour. The visitors were wild bees, honey-bees, flies and hover-flies. A total of fifty-six visited the flowers with yellow pebbles, while seven went to those with b'ack pebbles. This is very significant, especially as honey-bees and hover-flies are a usual part of the diet of this spider. Not only does the spider's colour-harmony help it to get a meal, but it often saves it from falling a prey to some passing bird. The camouflage of web spiders may also be considered as at the same time protective and aggressive.

Just as camouflage affords no protection to the spider's prey, so the spider itself, however well concealed, is not safe from the attack of parasitic ichneumon wasps and digging wasps (Pompilidae). These insects with uncanny instinct seek out certain spiders as hosts and deposit their eggs within them. Such wasps are among the most serious enemies of spiders. As Bristowe remarks, " The types of enemy with which a spider has to contend are so varied that we must never expect any one device to shelter it from *all* its enemies."

To summarise the position where spiders are concerned : camouflage provides little or no protection against the spider as hunter. Spiders themselves are well camouflaged, and this serves the double purpose of protecting them against certain of their enemies—those that hunt by sight—while at the same time giving them a better chance of capturing insects with good vision. The spider's own camouflage is, however, useless against the attack of parasitic wasps. The result appears to be that out of the very large spider population in a given area, many survive and many are destroyed : the balance of nature is maintained.

It is clear that when insects are in flight their camouflage is no longer effective. Swallows and their kin, wheeling at high speed through the air, with open beaks, take any winged creature that crosses their path. The swift predaceous dragonflies pay no attention to protective or warning colours. Bats, hunting in the half-lights, and in any case having very weak eyesight, destroy many a moth which has escaped during the daylight hours on account of its cryptic colouring. Small birds, however well concealed while hopping about in hedge or bush, are liable to be struck down by a sparrow-hawk when they fly in the open. Where nocturnal hunters are concerned, it may be taken as a general rule that hunting is by touch, scent and hearing rather than by sight.

There are interesting individual cases where what appears to be a perfect camouflage is of no avail against one particular enemy. The common shrimp, *Crangon*, shows detailed and perfect blending with a sandy or gravelly sea floor. But during the daytime, if a certain fish, the wrasse, is about, it is fatal for the shrimps to move. They must remain buried, with nothing but their eyes showing, and even then the wrasse will sometimes get at them. At night wrasse retire into rocky crevices to sleep, and then the shrimps are safe from this enemy at least.

Although honey-bees and wasps are avoided by most birds, they are taken by fly-catchers and bee-eaters. A rather similar case is that of cuckoos, which during their stay in Britain feed on caterpillars avoided by other birds on account of their irritating hairs or spines. Cuckoos make a point of eating, for instance, the " football-jersey " caterpillar of the cinnabar moth and the caterpillar of the magpie moth, both conspicuously coloured types distasteful to other insectivorous birds.

Both on general grounds and as the result of experiments, it appears that both cryptic and warning colours give relative freedom from attack by the Vertebrate animals (fish, frogs, toads, newts, reptiles, birds and mammals). Professor F. B. Sumner carried out experiments with penguins—birds which dive under water and pursue and capture fish. He kept numbers of mosquito fish for several weeks, some in black and some in white tanks, after which time one set had become black and the other pale buff or grey. Then, at the penguin's feeding time, he emptied equal numbers of pale and dark fish into a tank with black walls. Of the fish the penguins caught, 73% were pale and 27% were dark. When the experiment was repeated in a tank with pale grey walls, 61% of those eaten were dark and 38% pale. Clearly the fish which were less conspicuous in their surroundings had a better chance of survival. Fishermen sometimes make use of this knowledge: they keep the small fish to be used as bait in a white jar, so that

being conspicuous when dropped in the water, they are more likel
to lure a catch.

Young made several experiments with birds in captivity, offerin
them natural living food on backgrounds against which they tone
or contrasted in varying degree. In every case the less the pre
harmonised with its background the more certainly was it caugh
A long-eared owl, for example, chose house mice from the back
ground with which they contrasted most strongly on eleven out o
twelve occasions. How dangerous it is for an edible and defenceles
creature to contrast with its background under natural condition
is shown by the following instance. A "sport" or mutatio
occurred in a certain butterfly (*Colias philodice*) which affected
among other things, the colour of the caterpillars. These ar
normally the green of the clover leaves on which they feed, but th
mutants were a blue-green colour. Gerould, who noticed them
put a mixed batch of normal and blue-green caterpillars on clove
plants in the open, and left them exposed for ten minutes to th
attacks of sparrows. At the end of this time the only survivor
were those of clover-green colour. Among various experiment
made by Isely on the chance of survival of grasshoppers from th
attacks of birds is one that is both brief and conclusive. Forty
anaesthetised grasshoppers were placed on a plot of ground with
which they did not harmonise. Three bantams required just one
minute to find and eat every one. Another day, forty more anaesthetised hoppers were placed on the same plot, this time of a kin
that harmonised with the vegetation. By the end of one minut
the same three bantams had discovered and eaten only six.

In all cases of cryptic resemblance, stillness is an immense asset
Poulton noticed that so long as "stick" caterpillers remained still
green lizards generally failed to detect them, but the moment th
"sticks" moved they were snapped up. Regarding the Graylin
butterfly, Frohawk writes, "On several occasions I have seer
kestrels in pursuit of the grayling and have seen them try to
catch them on the wing, but they usually fail to do so. If missec
in the swoop the butterfly darts to the ground and becomes invisibl
to the bird. . . . The bird hovers a moment or two, scanning th
surface a few feet below, then rises again and waits until anothe
Grayling takes wing and gives it another chance, but more ofter
than not the butterfly escapes."

A cat was seen in pursuit of a mouse which ran across a flower
bed of dry grey-brown earth. The mouse stopped—so did the
cat, which remained tense and quivering, unable to see its prey
until it should move again.

WARNING COLORATION AND SURVIVAL

We turn now to examples of animals with warning colours, and the enquiry as to whether these protect their wearers. The first need of warning colours is that they should be bold and give the maximum contrast to the ordinary neutral setting of green and brown. Contrast in itself, as we have seen, is usually fatal to its wearer, but where red, orange, yellow, black and white are the colours concerned, survival usually results. We are at once tempted to ask, " Do hungry animals avoid these blatantly coloured species by instinct, or do they learn by bitter—often literally bitter—experience?" Where Vertebrates are concerned, the latter is usually the case wherever the matter has been put to the test of experiment.

Lloyd Morgan tested the matter on domestic chicks, moorhen chicks and ducklings. These tested everything offered them as food and learnt rapidly as a result of experience. Cinnabar caterpillars, soldier beetles and ladybirds, all warningly coloured, were tasted, and then avoided at once or after a second trial, on account of their unpleasant flavour. If a chick swallowed a honey-bee whole, and was not stung, it would peck at other bees, but if it was unlucky at the first attempt, it avoided in future not only bees, but also the similarly coloured but harmless drone-flies.

W. B. Cott carried out a very thorough and interesting series of experiments on toads, with regard to their eating of honey-bees. Beekeepers sometimes find that a toad locates itself near the alighting board and accounts for large numbers of bees. Thirty-three toads were used in the experiments, and the behaviour of each one recorded separately. Each toad, hungry because it had been without food for some days, was placed in turn on the alighting stage of a hive. It snapped up a bee, and, " if stung, closed its eyes and gulped and soon crawled to the edge of the stage and jumped off." It was replaced and its behaviour again watched. Ten of the thirty-three toads avoided bees entirely after the first unpleasant experience. Others took up to five days before they refused even to attempt to catch a bee; by this time they showed evident signs of fearing the insects. Thus the speed of learning varied considerably with individual toads. However, once the lesson was learned it was not forgotten, for when a fortnight later the toads were again placed on the alighting stage, they either avoided the bees at once or after far fewer trials than before.

Snakes and lizards, both wild and captive, have been seen to select frogs with cryptic colours from frogs with warning colours,

and house geckos, which hunt insects on walls and ceilings at night
capture some kinds of moths and beetles, but leave others untouched

Conclusive evidence that wild birds avoid nauseous, brightl
coloured insects was obtained by Kluijver. He worked for three
years with a colony of starlings whose feeding area was about 10
acres. He fitted some nestlings for a short period with a nec
collar which allowed them to swallow only partially food brough
by the parents. It was then possible to examine the food. O
the 3,307 butterflies, moths and (presumably) caterpillars brough
by the parent starlings, only three had warning colours, namel
one Burnet moth and two cinnabars. Among the 4,490 beetles
only two ladybirds were found. Of the 779 Hymenoptera, no
honey-bee or wasp was recorded, and only one digging wasp
The rest of the catch was of non-stinging types. In taking th
warningly-coloured but safe Hymenoptera, starlings show an un
usual amount of discrimination.

Some Russian scientists devised a neat method of examining th
food brought by parent birds to their young. A wooden box wa
arranged with a dummy nestling bird whose open beak was jus
below the level of an alighting platform for the parent. Youn
bird and platform were connected by wiring to an electric battery
As the parent bird perched on the platform she made an electri
contact which caused the nestling's beak to close on the food
pushed into it. When the parent flew away the electric contac
was broken: this caused the nestling's beak to open again, allowing
the food to fall into a jar beneath. The jar was examined at
regular intervals and the creatures it contained counted and
identified.

Some distasteful or dangerous creatures will, in time of danger
add to their warning colour the production of a nauseous smell
This often prevents a trial attack, which, even if not fatal, is cer
tainly an event to be avoided. There is the case of Alcock's
Himalayan bear, which was brought straight from its mother's
den to a large garden where it could roam at will. In the garden
were various kinds of grasshoppers with cryptic colouring, and a
black kind with bright red bands on the body and bright yellow
patches on the forewings—a very definite notice to "keep off"
The bear's master picked up one of these "blazer" grasshoppers
and it produced from its mouth a froth with a horrid smell. The
bear gave one sniff at the grasshopper and curled its lip. When
the master offered it a second time, the bear knocked it away
out of his hand.

Monkeys, being inquisitive creatures with quite marked likes and dislikes where food is concerned, provide useful data on the question as to how far insects with warning colours are distasteful to them, while those with protective colours are edible. Carpenter made extensive observations on this matter. Many kinds of insects were offered to or caught by these monkeys. One monkey was observed on 615 occasions, and 244 different species of insects comprised its menu during the course of these observations. The monkey sampled 143 insects with warning colours and found 120 of these distasteful and the remaining 23 good to eat. It is significant how closely the percentages in these groups agree. In the group with warning colours, about 16% were edible—that is, could be described as showing " false warning coloration ". In the group with cryptic colours about 17% were distasteful, and, judged from this aspect, might be described as showing " false cryptic colours ".

On thinking over this monkey's behaviour, one might at first condemn it as unintelligent and very slow to learn. On second thoughts, one can but admire its perseverance in the face of uncertainty. The position is rather like that of a child given a large box of chocolates of many shapes and with varied kinds of decoration. The child likes soft centres and dislikes hard ones. She samples a round kind with a rose petal on top—it has a delicious soft centre with strawberry flavour. Next she tries another of just the same shape, but without the petal, and bites hard on—a nut. There are still other round kinds: is it worth risking a bite in case they contain that delicious strawberry centre? There is not much doubt as to the answer. So with the monkey; it was worth risking a bite at a brightly coloured insect in case it had just the good flavour of the first bright one picked up by chance.

The results obtained from watching monkeys are typical of the general state of affairs, namely that the *majority* of creatures with warning colours are distasteful, or dangerous, or both, but some are harmless and palatable. The *majority* of creatures with cryptic colouring are harmless and edible, but there are exceptions. It is evident that in Nature it is safe to take nothing for granted. Thus it is best—after the period of trial and error—to avoid all prey with warning colours. Where soberly-coloured creatures are concerned, if they *should* turn out to be distasteful, the only remedy is to spit them out again as soon as possible.

Were all predatory animals to behave like Carpenter's monkeys, warning colours would be of little avail, but the chicks and toads which learn by experience and then refuse all prey marked with such colours show the more usual mode of behaviour. A constant but relatively small toll must be taken of warningly coloured creatures by this process of trial and error. Another point to be borne in mind is that the term "distasteful" is relative, for tastes vary considerably in the animal world. We have seen that ants are distasteful to spiders, but there are birds that eat them freely, and they are the main diet of the anteater. Hedgehogs hunt vipers, and the mongoose is the self-appointed destroyer of cobras. A few animal types, such as the skunk, badger and Poison Bully toad, seem to be immune from attack except by man. Others, such as "flies", earthworms, common frogs and rabbits, seem almost designed to provide food for all and sundry. Between these extremes come types in danger from numbers of enemies varying from several to one only. "Je mange et je suis mangé."

From the brief evidence reviewed in this chapter—and there is much more available—it appears that camouflage mostly takes effect where the larger creatures are concerned—anything from the size of a ladybird upwards. The better developed the eyesight of a creature, the greater the significance of camouflage where it is concerned. Protective and warning colours assist their wearers, but cannot ensure survival. This is really self-evident, or how could predatory creatures come by their food, or the too-exuberant multiplication of vegetarian types be kept in check?

CHAPTER IX

WHAT IS THE REAL SIGNIFICANCE OF CAMOUFLAGE?

THE natural world abounds in examples of animal camouflage. The strongest upholders of its effectiveness, its reality, and its value in the struggle for existence are experienced naturalists, people long trained in accurate observation of animals in their wild condition. So there is no doubt that, so far as we can trust our own eyes, camouflage is a fact in nature.

There are two main theories that seek to explain the facts as observed, and brief reference will be made to them. One theory is that the colour, and to some extent the form, of an animal is the outcome of the chemical and physical conditions of its environment, using the term in its widest meaning. Writing of spiders which live habitually in caves or in cellars, Bristowe states that they tend to become long-legged and are pale. The formation of melanin pigment depends on a process of oxidation which is retarded in very dim light. Absence of light and high humidity also tend to restrict the formation of chitin, with resulting elongation of legs and spines. A notable kind of newt, the Olme (*Proteus*), found in the Balkans, shows the results of age-long exposure of its race to the darkness of underground caves. It is blind, and must be kept in semi-darkness, for its pale skin blackens if exposed to light. The skin has the latent materials for making melanin,* but the action does not take place in the absence of light. An example of this creature may be seen at the London Zoo.

There is, in animals, a long-recognised correlation between dark skin colour and high humidity, and between pale colour and arid conditions. It is now known that great humidity and high temperature favour the formation of black eumelanins; great heat and aridity give yellow and red-brown phaeomelanins, and lower temperatures give grey and grey-brown forms of melanin. Experiments made in keeping certain kinds of birds in an atmosphere more humid than is natural to them, have in some cases caused the birds to darken. A desert-living weaver bird from Australia, for example, darkens when living in moist air.

Then there are many cases of local races which differ from one another in colour. There is in New Mexico a large area covered by black larva, and near it another region where the ground is of white gypsum. These black and white districts are surrounded by rocky areas of neutral tone. A " mouse-coloured " type of mouse lives in the rocky areas, of which a black species is found on the black larva beds and a white species on the white gypsum area. The yellow-wattled lapwing, which breeds throughout the greater part of India, nests in depressions in the bare ground. Its eggs are usually earth-coloured with dark markings, and are extremely difficult to see. But on part of the Malabar coast, where the soil is brick-red with nodules of black ironstone, the eggs are various shades of brick-red and have black or brown specks and patches, making them again almost invisible. Possibly the radiations given off by the two kinds of earth affect the birds and mammals concerned, resulting in alterations of colour, but more probably they are due to the sum-total of the local physiographical conditions.

Present-day genetics has, however, another explanation for the colour harmony of local races with their environment: they are described as the result of preadaptation. It is thought that among neutral coloured mice in the rocky areas of New Mexico, for example, mutations occurred which caused some descendants to be much darker and others much paler than their ancestors. The dark and pale forms had a better chance of survival when living

* The melanin precursor, tyrosine, and the enzyme tyrosinase.

on the black and the white areas respectively, and in time became fully harmonised with them in colour.

Preadaptation is no doubt responsible in part for the blind fauna of caves. Animal types which already had poor sight and avoided bright light would tend to enter caves, and later evolution would reduce their eyesight still further.

The second main theory to account for camouflage (one cannot do justice to either in a few words) is that of variations acted upon by natural selection; it is, in fact, the general theory of evolution. Protective resemblance is accounted for somewhat after this manner. Among a number of greenish insects living among green leaves, one was hatched that was by chance, as the result of a mutation, the exact colour of the leaves. While many of its kind were destroyed, this one survived and left offspring. By the operation of heredity, there would be among its offspring more individuals that approached the " correct " green than in the previous generation: so that after a very large number of generations all these insects were of the same colour as their food plant. Those that did not match had been weeded out by natural selection. In a similar way, for a true " leaf " insect to evolve, additional points of camouflage, such as flatness, leafy outline, markings suggesting veins, and so on, are assumed to arrive by occasional mutations of a favourable nature. This rather implies that a succession of inheritable variations (mutations) took place, some at least of which were favourable to the insect, and that these were retained by selection.

Variations are liable to be very " chance " occurrences as regards their usefulness to the creature concerned. But once they occur there is no doubt that natural selection acts upon them. Harrison gives a clear example of variations which proved useful to some moths and fatal to others. The moths concerned (*Oporabia autumnata*) occur on Eston Moor, Yorkshire. Early in the nineteenth century, the pinewood in which these moths lived, and which contained isolated clumps of birch and alder, became divided into two parts by half a mile of heather and bracken. After some years a gale blew down the pine trees in one wood and they were replaced by birch. In the other wood the pine trees flourished but the birch and alder were dying out. This was in 1885, and from that time on one colony of moths lived in a pinewood, the other in a wood of birch and alder.

By 1907 the two colonies could be distinguished by a number of characteristics, including colour. " In the pinewood about 96% of the moths belonged to a dark form and 4% to a light one. I the birchwood about 85% were light and 15% were dark. This difference appears to be due to selective elimination in the pine-wood of the more conspicuous paler moths by owls, nightjars and bats. Although here the dark moths outnumbered the pale by more than 25 to 1, the majority of moths eaten by these predators (as indicated by discarded wings) belonged to the light variety . . . these are being progressively eliminated." Once the dark and light forms of moth appeared, natural selection took its course upon them. But what caused the two forms?

Those who do not favour the idea that protective resemblance is mainly the result of chemical and physical forces playing directly on the responsive organisms, quote examples where different colour forms occur under almost identical conditions. In the same valley, and at the same height above sea-level, may be found buff and tawny-coloured animals living on pale desert patches, and black forms of the same animals living on patches of black larva. We cannot, however, overlook the different chemical and physical conditions on the two types of ground, which may affect the colour of the populations concerned. Cott considers that a compromise can be arrived at between the two points of view, something after this manner. Pronounced differences of humidity in the air may be able to bring about changes in pigment formation which become inherited, while selection in favour of concealing coloration may enhance these effects. We are, however, still left to explain why the direct action of physical forces should produce effects which are appropriate to the animal's needs, and so can be preserved by selection. Cott is of the opinion that whatever gives protection from predatory enemies is the most decisive factor in operation.

Now, whenever an animal exhibits camouflage which involves many details of form and colour, together with some special behaviour or posture, it is difficult to avoid the conclusion that some unitary idea or purpose is behind the final result. Cott is of the opinion that when an animal combines in itself *all* theoretical optical principles tending to concealment, this cannot be explained by chance. Ouspensky points out that in any accurate example of mimicry, very many factors together constitute the disguise. According to evolutionary theory, the variations which produce these factors ("characters" in Mendel's terminology) are to a great extent accidental. Such an explanation does not take into consideration the mathematical impossibility of this kind of "accidental" series of combinations and repetitions. "When one trait makes an animal invisible in its surroundings, as a white hare in snow, it may be explained 'scientifically'. But when the number of such traits becomes almost incalculable, such an explanation loses all logical possibility."

Recent discoveries in genetics bring such matters more within the range of possibility. J. B. S. Haldane in his *Causes of Evolution* and Julian Huxley in his *Evolution : the Modern Synthesis* set out a view of the position which gives far more satisfaction. Variations are now known to occur along certain lines, not at random in every direction. As well as the earlier idea of each gene being responsible for a single character, such as tallness or shortness in peas, and a mutation which affects a gene altering only one character at a time, the *multiple* effect of a single gene is now well known. For instance, as stated by Haldane, the gene Ch in *Primula sinensis* incises the petals, doubles the number of sepals, breaks up the bracts, produces more compact habit, increases crimping of leaves in the presence of other genes, and so on. So that in the case of a leaf insect a mutation affecting a single gene could produce several leaf-like characters simultaneously. This may also account for instances where some change of form or colour proves detrimental to its wearer.

It is also known that a gene does not always change abruptly, but by a number of small steps (multiple allelomorphs appear which bring about very slight changes in the original type of gene). This allows changes in fur colour, for example, to take place by very slight stages, trying out their success, as it were, against the vigilance of natural selection. This is more likely to produce useful adaptations than are random variations of conspicuous type. Rapid forms of evolution can also occur as the result of hybridisation, and a new combination of several genes can give a result quite distinct from the summation of their effects one at a time.

VARIETIES OF SEEING

Assuming, then, that there is some truth in the whole concept of animal camouflage, let us enquire further into the facts. From a study of the eye of certain animals it is evident that the kind of world they see varies greatly. As regards the actual sensory impressions made on the eyes, the higher mammals, and the birds, are in much the same position as ourselves. Even so, we must allow for slight differences in colour vision, and for absence of this faculty. Cott has photographed a number of what appear to the human eye to be green animals at rest on green leaves. In the photographs, the *tone* of animal and leaf appears the same. But when the same subjects are photographed with infra-red plates, in some cases the animals still harmonise with their leafy background, in others they stand out in vivid contrast. An animal with eyes capable of using infra-red rays would at once detect the latter examples, and protective resemblance would not exist. Where colour camouflage is used for war purposes, it is found that colour-blind persons see readily through devices which baffle the eyes of those with normal colour vision. So what conceals to one kind of animal may reveal to another.

Then there is the question of dimensional effect. Animals with binocular sight, such as the cat, may receive a three-dimensional view, allowing them to judge exact position more nearly; but this form of vision is not essentially connected with *consciousness* of a three-dimensional field. The majority of animals have, like the cow, only monocular vision, and a general flat impression must be received which gives little information as to the relative distances of objects. As regards the interpretation of impressions received by the eyes, it is stated on good authority that most mammals— for example the cat and the horse—cannot distinguish their own movement relative to that of their environment. When a cat walks up a road, the trees and houses appear, to the cat, to move steadily towards it, by what are really the apparent changes of relative position due to his motion.* The changing shapes of objects, which we become accustomed to connect with perspective, remain to these animals changing shapes, and, if unfamiliar, these may prove startling. A horse sometimes takes fright and bolts because strange objects appear to come towards it suddenly and unexpectedly.

The importance of immobility in camouflage has already been mentioned. It subserves concealment because, whatever the type of eye, it can always detect movement of a single object relative to the landscape as a whole. Hence if a rabbit suspects danger it remains quite still, watching for a movement that will reveal some enemy it cannot recognise while stationary.

In creatures with a nervous system so different from our own— for instance, insects, worms and molluscs—we can know little of what is actually " seen ", even though it is known that the eyes form an image. The capacity of bees' eyes for using ultra-violet wave-lengths allows them to appreciate effects which we cannot. An example of these effects may be seen in the mineral gallery at the London Natural History Museum. This shows a scientific " Cave of Aladdin ". A group of minerals (fluorspar; willemite, $ZnSO_4$; aragonite) which in ordinary daylight have quite insignificant colours, can be lit by ultra-violet rays, under which they

* See Ouspensky.

become fluorescent and glow with remarkable light and colour. If the alighting board of a beehive is painted "white" by using zinc white or Titan white paint, this is presumably seen by bees as intense blue-green, and is very effective in guiding them home.

Professor Hogben has drawn attention to many errors which arise from failure to appreciate differences in wave-length given out by various pigments which are described as being of the same colour. "The assertion that a particular type of response occurs when an animal is placed on a red background might signify the direct effect of rays in the red region or be the result of reducing radiation in the green region." A table showing the relative reflection by two "red" and two "yellow" pigments is given in Appendix V. Actually, any monochromatic light can be "matched" by a mixture of other wave-lengths, that is, it gives the same colour sensation to our eyes.

The actual light intensity transmitted through monochromatic glass plates or gelatine filters also varies greatly. Yellow glass lets through more total light, irrespective of wave-length, than red, and red glass more light than blue, when all the sheets are of uniform thickness. Since light intensity has such marked effects on the eyes of animals, it is clear that this matter must be rigidly controlled and measured during experimental work.

Another point to be borne in mind is that many camouflaged animals never see themselves, or see at most but a fraction of their surface. Still less can they see themselves in relation to their environment. The sea slug, merging in perfect colour harmony with the sponge and coralline weed on which it rests, has a small spherical eye on each feeler, capable at most of viewing a tiny area an inch or so in front of its head. By bending the tentacles outwards it could see its own "shoulder", but no more. We can be fairly certain that a herring has never seen anything but its own tail. A tortoise which was kept as a pet for some years and showed well-developed intelligence, was on one occasion shown its own reflection in a mirror. Its behaviour showed that it recognised "tortoise" at once, but certainly did not know that the tortoise was itself.

We have also the curious occurrence of "dummy" eyes, placed as though with definite intent, and with cognition of what a Vertebrate eye looks like, yet displayed not only by Vertebrates, but also by adult insects with compound eyes, and even by caterpillars.

The glistening eye of the Vertebrate, with its round black pupil, is a very conspicuous object, likely to betray its owner's presence. So much is this the case that a variety of special devices for camoulage of the eye are shown by animals with cryptic colouring. Yet other animals sport this very same target or bull's eye effect for purposes of deflecting attack. In such cases the false eye is somewhere well away from the real eye. Such eyelike markings adorn the feathers of the Argus pheasant, and occur on the scales of lizards and snakes, and on tropical fishes. They also appear on many different kinds of insects, which may or may not be thought to cognize the meaning of such markings.

These "false eyes" certainly deflect attack from vulnerable parts, or prevent attack altogether by scaring away potential enemies. The Eyed Hawk Moth (*Smerinthus ocellatus*) will, if in danger of attack while at rest, raise its fore wings and display on its hind wings a pair of large round eyes. At dusk, when this moth is on the wing, these eyes are quite startlingly lifelike. Several kinds of butterflies have eye-spots, in various positions on the wings, but always well away from the body. Near such markings, the wings quite commonly show damage caused by the beak of an attacking bird. Typical of many examples where false eyes produce a sudden startling effect is the mantis (*Pseudocreobotra wahlbergi*). "When alarmed it elevates its wing covers above its back like two signal arms—each of which bears on the *dorsal* surface a conspicuous ocellus, thus directing towards the intruder a somewhat formidable, not to say astonishing appearance." Such a display can save the life of the mantis.

Mimicry of form, colour, posture and movement often has clear advantages. But how can we construe the mimicry of sounds shown by birds such as the starling? Mimicry of sound in wild birds at least, is just as unconscious, as "purposeless", as other forms of mimicry. Where a bird such as a raven or parrot has been associated with human beings for some time, however, the case is altered, and it is difficult to avoid the conclusion that some of their remarks are made with definite intent—to attract attention, cause a bustle and so on.

Then there are curious instances where the colour of an animal is changed through the stimulus of *touch*. If a tree frog (*Hyla*) is placed on a rough material which gives a stimulus like that of bark, the frog becomes grey or black, but if placed on a smooth surface suggesting a leaf, the frog becomes green. The Octopus and the Lesser Octopus (*Eledone*) have touch cells on the suckers of their arms. If these come into contact with some hard surface to which they can cling, the animals become dark, but if placed on a surface comparable to sand, where they can take no hold, the animals assume a light speckled appearance. As an example of creatures with a deep-seated rhythm which causes them to darken by day and pale by night, we may cite *Idothea*, a crustacean found between tide-marks, and looking not unlike a long, shiny wood-louse. *Idothea* retains its periodic colour change for eight weeks or more while kept in darkness the whole time.

The circumstances so far reviewed all point to the conclusion that where camouflage is concerned, the effects must differ according to the visual and psychological capacity of the spectators, and that in many cases the camouflaged animal is unaware of any such effects. But since colour schemes and camouflage are found throughout the animal kingdom, irrespective of whether the wearer can or cannot appreciate the fact, and sometimes irrespective of any survival value, we must look deeper for the causes.

ACTION OF LIGHT UPON MATTER; PHYSICAL AND CHEMICAL RESULTS

The causes appear to lie in the fundamental action of light upon living matter. We are often reminded that all life upon our planet depends on the interaction of sunlight with the chlorophyll pigment of the green plant. Reactions of the greatest importance also take place between sunlight and the pigments of animals.

Light cannot act unless it is absorbed. According to their composition and colour, animal pigments absorb some or all the rays of the spectrum. One of the results of this capacity is the absorption of heat, and regulation of temperature. The absorption of heat by melanin pigment has value where frog spawn is concerned. At the time of laying, the frog's egg has, on top, an " animal pole " covered with black pigment, and below a " vegetable pole " coloured yellow by yolk granules. The black pigment absorbs heat rays from the March sunshine, and the curved surface of the jelly helps by acting as a lens and concentrating light upon the animal pole. Increased warmth assists the development of the egg. Hashimoto found that rabbits' noses absorb heat, and this must be the case with other mammals, such as the dog. Possibly this has the advantage of increasing the action of the sensory cells in the skin of the nose. Dark hair and fur must also absorb heat.

As regards temperature regulation, a frog has in its skin melanin pigment cells capable of concentration to pin-point size or dispersal to give a fairly complete covering. In the latter condition a large surface is presented which absorbs any available heat. It so happens that low temperatures reflexly cause expansion of the pigment cells, though other factors may lessen this effect. (See Chap. VII). High temperatures tend to concentrate the pigment cells. In general, these reactions are true for other vertebrates which show colour change.

The use of the absorptive power of melanin in temperature control is shown in quite a different way in the human subject. Here, according to Humphris, the melanin pigment of the skin is primarily a screen, which protects the underlying tissues from excess of light, and especially of ultra-violet rays. This is accomplished by absorbing the rays and converting them into heat (a very small quantity) which is then sweated away. (Persons who do not pigment, or bronze well, do not benefit so markedly from ultra-violet treatment.) The screening action of melanin " can be demonstrated by isolating melanin as a fine powder and mixing with water. The resulting mixture or suspension protects the palm of the hand from the sun's rays as concentrated by a burning glass." No further comment is needed on the dark skins of natives of equatorial regions. The protective value of pigments in animals of transparent texture has already been referred to. The optic nerve and other structures in the eye-stalk of the prawn would be fully exposed by the transparent shell and tissues were it not for the pigment screen provided by a group of chromatophores.

The chemical action of light on pigment is a matter of great importance in animal life. Pigment can serve as a transformer of light energy into energy expended in some chemical action. According to Humphris, the absorption of sunlight by melanin in the human subject probably causes a reflex stimulation of internal glandular secretions, especially adrenalin. Perhaps this accounts for the tendency to assertiveness shown by the townsman after a week or so of outdoor life! Calcium metabolism is also affected, as is well known, by the action of sunlight on the ergosterol in the skin, with the resulting formation of Vitamin D. On the negative side, the effects of spending much of the day in the darkness or semi-darkness of a mine are manifest in the depressed and resentful psychological condition sometimes found among miners, which appears to be physical in origin. In contrast with this is the general cheerfulness of the sailor, who gets all the light there is.

A familiar but none the less impressive example of the chemical action of light is shown in photography. Here wave-lengths reflected from the objects photographed affect the chemicals of the plate or film in such a manner as to reproduce those objects accurately, by bleaching of the exposed areas. (Photo-graphy: drawing by means of light).

Much experimental work has been done with a view to deciding the effects of various colours on animals, and there is no doubt that different parts of the spectrum give markedly different results. To obtain a pure colour, light of a known wave-length (monochromatic light) is used, or white light falling on a background which reflects light of a known wave-length.

When Pieris caterpillars are exposed to such lights their skin pigments are variously affected. Ultra-violet, violet and blue light to decreasing extents favour the development of white and of dark pigments. In green light both pigments almost disappear, in yellow light they do so completely. Under orange and red light, white pigment is completely removed and a new pigment is produced. Under infra-red light, much white pigment appears. Where animals have coloured chromatophores, and a colour sense, interesting results are to be expected. According to Von Buddenbrock, light of a primary type has a direct action on chromatophores of complementary colour in the cuttlefish. Thus blue light causes yellow chromatophores to expand, and yellow light expands those of red-violet colour. He is also of the opinion that by absorption of light in these pigments, chemical changes are produced in the chromatophores which stimulate the muscle fibres responsible for their expansion and contraction.

It is worth reviewing again the relation between wave-length, eyes, and colour change as shown by shrimps, frogs, fishes, and their kin. In the toad *Xenopus* there are two distinct areas of the retina, each reflexly causing the liberation of a different hormone controlling colour change. One of these areas (the " floor " elements of the retina) is known to be specially sensitive to red rays. In the shrimp *Crangon*, red light permits complete and quick contraction of all coloured pigments, while under blue light this cannot occur completely.

When any of these animals which show typical colour change are placed on a background of red, yellow, black, or white, their pigment cells assume the best relative conditions of contraction and expansion to suit the particular background. If they remain for some time on any one background, such as red, then the actual amount of red pigment is increased. Should they be placed on a background of some colour not represented in their normal state, even so, after many weeks, flat fishes are able to produce pigment of this colour. Thus a specific light stimulus, striking the eyes and conveyed to the brain, calls out a material response in the form of pigment. There is no obvious connection between the quality of the stimulus and the result in the pigmentary effector system.

It is not difficult to understand how, in certain insects, exposure to different wave-lengths directly affects the skin pigmentation.

The enzyme tyrosinase is present in the blood, and this, on exposure to light, acts on tyrosine with resulting formation of melanin. Yellow rays cause local acidity which almost stops the action of tyrosinase, while ultra-violet rays cause an alkaline condition followed by great activity of tyrosinase and much development of melanin. This is a very clear case of the chemical action of light directly affecting pigmentation. But how, in animals whose skin is not directly susceptible to electro-magnetic rays, yet where these act upon the *eyes*, does light produce its manifestations in pigmented matter?

Przibram's theory, put forward some years ago, is that the alteration of tyrosinase in such animals takes place in the eye itself (the retina and choroid have an extensive circulation), and from thence the products spread over the whole body. Presumably other chemical alterations occur which affect the formation of other pigments. He conceives the eye as an organ of electro-chemical change. Later work and statements fall in line, and we may be nearing a complete description of the link between certain wave-lengths and certain types of matter. Yapp writes, " It may be assumed for physical reasons, that in all cases where a structure is sensitive to light, the latter is responsible for initiating a photo-chemical reaction, probably with the production of some substance which acts on a nerve." In this case, however, the change is very local and does not affect other organs.

Another definite example of the chemical action of light is the metabolism of fat which takes place in the red pigment cells of the chameleon prawn, and the fact that light quickens the synthesis of the eye-stalk hormone in prawns and their kin. There seems little doubt that the chemical action of light upon pigment is the basis from which the work of internal or endocrine secretions is derived.

Brief mention must be made of the use of coloured light (excluding dubious psychological colour-therapy) in preventing damage to the skin by disease. The use of Finsen red light prevents the pitting due to smallpox (see *Extra Pharmacopœia*). Such work, once derided as mere superstition, is now seen to have a basis in fact. There is also evidence that a considerable amount of yellow or green light (used for lighting a dining table for example) can interfere with the gastric functions to a marked degree. From antiquity to the present day, colours have been traditionally associated with emotional and mental states—blue for aspiration, green for jealousy, and so on. It is never advisable completely to ignore beliefs which have existed for centuries, as there is sometimes a sub-

stratum of truth in the ideas.   The significance of dreams has, for
instance, been recently vindicated by Freudian discoveries.

Finally, it must be remembered that living creatures are subjected
to the action of electro-magnetic waves (waves of the sun, or of the
electro-magnetic field of the earth) throughout the twenty-four
hours.*   These set up within them an ever-recurrent biological
rhythm.   " Many of these vibrations are not only transmitted to
the living organism through the various senses, but they are also
set up in the body. . . . The vibration of the organs of vision,
hearing and voice must be regarded as periodic changes within
cells of the nervous system, reaching down to the region of atomic
and sub-atomic. . . . If there were no variation in the quality
and quantity of light, life and growth would be impossible."   According to Lord Clifford of Chudleigh, different colour rays predominate at different hours of the diurnal cycle.   " Living processes
are sustained by the rhythmic action of a succession of colour rays."
Once more we return to the sun as the physical source and sustainer
of life in all its endless variety.

THE SIGNIFICANCE OF CAMOUFLAGE

After this digression regarding the physical and chemical action
of light upon pigment, and their far-reaching effects on the life
processes of animals, we may ask how these may be brought to
bear on the significance of camouflage.

Physical and chemical conditions are clearly of the utmost importance; indeed, they form and condition the organism to an
extensive degree.   To a considerable extent they determine the
type and distribution of its pigments.   For instance, the typical
condition of counter-shading—dark back grading to pale belly—
is partly due to the conditions under which melanin is formed,
the more light a surface receives, the more melanin is produced.
Such factors alone, however, cannot possibly account for the intricacies of camouflage.   Since all elements of camouflage are
really adaptive features, they must be accounted for in the same
manner as other adaptations of structure and physiology.

The basic question is whether camouflage can be considered in
any sense conscious or intentional.   To this Julian Huxley gives a
definite " No."   He writes, " The purpose manifested in evolution

* " The interesting studies that have been made at the Harvard Medical
School, the Loomas Laboratory, and elsewhere . . . offer a suggestion
that the electromagnetic field of the earth and changes in it may have
more to do with our reactions than we have even supposed."—H. T.
Stetson.

whether in adaptation, specialisation, or biological progress, is only an apparent purpose. It is as much a product of blind forces as is the falling of a stone to earth or the ebb and flow of the tides. It is we who have read purpose into evolution, as earlier men projected will and emotion into inorganic phenomena like storm or earthquake." Haldane considers that evolution, including adaptation, can be explained in terms of the capacity of organisms for variation, and the action of natural selection on these variations. "This excludes the action of a mind higher than that of the evolving individuals, except in so far as such a mind is concerned in the general nature of the universe and its laws." The true scientific attitude is shown by these writers.

The work of science is to describe phenomena rather than to explain them. But frequently, because a good deal has been described, it is assumed that a full explanation has been given. As Haldane writes, " Genetics can give us an explanation of why two fairly similar organisms, say a black and a white cat, are different. It gives us much less information as to why they are alike. In the same way a complete theory of evolution . . . would give us little direct information concerning the nature of life."

It is permissible, however, even if for mere human satisfaction, to entertain a less completely detached view-point; to conceive of " Nature ", or the " Soul of the World ", as manifest in all living things that spring from the earth—a localised part of whatever is concerned in " the general nature of the universe and its laws ". This is nothing more or less than regarding " the world " as a unity or solidarity. Certain aspects of · Nature, such as beauty, and what Haldane describes as " inexhaustible queerness ", are distinctive attributes.

There is a very marked tendency in Nature towards general harmony of effect, towards the decorative. The fine lines of trees, the tapestry of a woodland ground flora, the mosaics, spirals and rosettes are but a few examples of such things in plant growth. Bare and unsightly places are soon made pleasing to the eye by their green covering, arranged with regard to the plant's need for light and space, but always with a result harmonious to the eye. The stump left by a fallen tree soon bears a graceful design in moss and ivy. Nature is a landscape artist, and an artist down to the finest details.

Animal life conforms to the general condition that everything shall be in keeping, though it must be borne in mind that contrast is itself sometimes an element of harmony. It is not merely " protective " that tree-dwellers should be green, and desert life clad in

buff and tawny shades. To appear as a " blot on the landscape '
would be contrary to what Ouspensky calls the " good taste o
Nature ". But brightly coloured flowers are an adornment, anc
so are brightly coloured birds and insects.

Ouspensky takes an attractive view of the subject of camouflage
He views Nature as having not only a strong trend to the decorative,
but to the theatrical as well—the tendency of creatures to appear
different from what they really are, the endless pageant of disguise
and masquerade. " A peacock dresses itself in round sun-flecks,
which fall on the ground from the rays passing through the foliage."
Among insects, especially in certain countries, there is a strong
tendency not to be themselves, but to resemble a green leaf, a patch
of lichen or a pebble. The more restricted the habitat, the more
will it take this as a copy.

" Who or what dresses up, who or what strives to be or to appear
something it is not? Obviously not the individual insect: it is
only a costume. . . . In the phenomena of decorativeness, in the
shapes and colours of living creatures, in the phenomena of mimicry,
even in ' protectiveness ', there can be seen a general plan, intention
and aim; and very often this plan is not utilitarian at all. What
then can it be? It is *fashion*, fashion in Nature ! "

Perhaps Maeterlinck had something of this kind in mind when
he wrote as follows in *The Life of the Ant*: " We have only to
assemble on a sheet of paper a few faces belonging to different
species of workers or soldiers, and we have a collection of masks
such as no carnival mask-maker of Nice or Venice has ever
imagined." This quotation is amplified by another extract from the
same work, referring to ants of the genus *Colobopsis*, which provide
an example of special protective resemblance.*

We now know that Nature achieves these effects of decoration
and camouflage partly by minute changes, but also by sudden and
often strange mutations. These facts incline us to presume the
existence of some power in Nature herself which directs the appear-

---

* " One of the most curious of these masks is that worn by the soldier
who is also a door-keeper. Or, to be precise, she is not a door-keeper, but
her head, monstrously specialised, is itself the door, fitting exactly, like a
stopper, into the entrance to the nest. If this nest is installed in a stem of
bamboo, for example, the head of the door-keeper assumes the appearance
and colour of the stem; if it is in the trunk of an old pear tree it is camouflaged like the bark of the pear tree. We find a whole series of inter-
mediary forms, from the full door-keeper or living door, to the semi-door-
keeper, the deputy door-keeper, the candidate, the amateur, etc., whose
organs appear to determine their destiny—unless indeed it is the destiny
that determines the organs."

ance and stabilising of new traits. Probably something akin to our concept of "sentience" must be allowed to all matter—"responsiveness". One remembers the tentative suggestion of Sir James Jeans that some mutations may be caused by cosmic rays, which are extra-terrestrial forces.* From this point of view it is legitimate to suppose that what are called the animal and vegetable kingdoms are the result of complicated work done in what Ouspensky terms the "Great Laboratory".

Another postulate is made by Sir John Hammerton: "The suggestion is, then, that the mutations which are the basis of evolution are the results of the chance bombardment of the molecules which are genes, by the waves of earth radiation."†

Such an idea would help to explain such strange occurrences as the bee and spider orchids—flowers which appear to "mimic" the bee or spider. Does the insect always "copy" the flower or plant? May not the same "idea" that produced the flower produce in the same guise the insect which so nearly resembles it, and is responsible for its pollination? It is said that a flower such as the Monkshood is adapted by reason of form, colour and the position of its nectar, to the visits of the bumble-bee. The tongue of the bee, its sensory apparatus and its behaviour may equally well be said to be adapted to visiting and pollinating the monkshood. Both are aspects of the same unitary concept: their spatial separation is of little moment.

To sum up the position, there is the scientific view point that living things and all their attributes are the result of purely fortuitous processes; though even the concept of "fortuitous processes" is only a human interpretation of data as far as collected up to the moment. There are also various philosophic modes of regarding the significance of life. The authors at present incline to the view that a form of sentience, or responsiveness, must be allowed to all matter, manifest in organic life in a mode for convenience described as "Nature". That science describes but cannot explain, and that since "matter" is after all nothing but a transitory arrangement of electronic energy, it is doubtful if any explanation that results from three-dimensional thinking, and sensory (to a great extent optical) impressions, can hope to approach the facts as they really are.

* In the laboratory, mutations are produced by X-rays.
† *Practical Knowledge for All*, p. 63, Vol. 6.

CHAPTER X

CONTROL OF COLOUR CHANGE IN VERTEBRATE ANIMALS

In all the lower vertebrate groups there are animals that show colour change. In birds and mammals, where the skin is concealed by feathers or by fur, colour change by means of chromatophores does not exist. In various arctic and northern forms, however, the fur or feathers show seasonal changes. The ptarmigan, willow grouse, Arctic fox and stoat, for example, blend with their summer surroundings and assume in winter a dress of white which blends with their snow-clad surroundings.

Where colour change occurs, there is also a more or less evident fixed or permanent pattern, independent of the changing nature of the other areas. This pattern may consist merely of a darker back and paler underside, or it may be of lines and patches variously arranged. The chromatophore system permeates these areas with a fixed pattern, under some conditions almost causing its obliteration, under others making it more marked. Frogs show this permanent pattern very clearly, especially in markings on the hind limbs and on the head, and it is well developed in lizards such as the horned "toad" and in some species of chameleon. In flat fishes only this fixed pattern is lacking.

The Vertebrate chromatophore is a single cell, freely branched, and almost always contains only one pigment at a time. In the embryos and larvae of fish the chromatophores show great amoeboid activity, and it is generally thought that the amoeboid chromatophore develops into the adult form whose branches are no longer movable. It would appear that when a chromatophore "expands" or "contracts", the pigment streams into or retreats from these preformed branches or paths; traces of the walls of the branches have been seen in contracted chromatophores. A photograph of the same chromatophore expanded, allowed to contract, then expanded again, shows complete similarity in form between the two expanded conditions. The mechanism for the dispersion or concentration of the pigment within the chromatophore is not yet fully understood.

It is interesting that in the Vertebrate groups which on other grounds appear to form an evolutionary sequence—elasmobranchs (cartilaginous fish such as skate and dogfish), amphibia and reptiles —colour change is first found as a process which takes a considerable time, but it becomes more rapid, until in the reptiles it is very quick. This increase in rate is accompanied by the change from slow hormone control to rapid nerve control of the process. There are many physiological processes in which hormone action is far slower than nerve action (with the exception of adrenalin), and humoral control is usually considered the more archaic method. In all groups the direct primary response of the chromatophores to light is still found. But the pigment movements, from being independent of any control by the animal concerned, come first under hormone and then under nerve control.

Cyclostomes, which include the archaic lampreys and hagfish, fall into line with the groups already mentioned.* The bony fish, or teleosts, are in many points of structure peculiar and specialised, and do not appear to come into the main evolutionary sequence of the vertebrates. In these fish colour change is typically rapid and is controlled by the nervous system, though hormone control also occurs in certain instances.

A. HUMORAL CONTROL

Elasmobranchs. Many elasmobranchs show very marked colour change. The monkfish (*Rhina squatina*) and some species of skate (*Raia maculata* and *R. brachiura*) become very dark all over when on a dark background, while on pale sand or gravel or in a white tank they are very light-coloured with grey markings. Species of dogfish appear to change only slightly, but microscopic examination shows a wide range of response of their pigment cells. (Plate 13.)

Skates, rays and dogfish are fairly shallow-water fish. Skates and rays rest and feed to a great extent on the sea bottom, and dogfish often do likewise, but dogfish are very agile swimmers, and pursue shoals of fish swimming near the sea surface. Skate and dogfish take from one to three days to become completely adapted to a change of background. They have a quite simple system of epidermal and dermal melanophores, the latter being larger and more branched and playing the major part in the colour change. There are also orange-yellow pigment cells (xanthophores). All types of pigment cells are controlled by the pituitary gland. Adaptation to a dark background is made and retained by a hormone produced in the neuro-intermediate lobe of the pituitary, and adaptation to a white background made and retained by a hormone produced in the anterior lobe of the pituitary. The eyes are the only receptors for background stimulus in elasmobranch fishes. There is one exception to the purely hormone control in

* It is of interest that the pineal acts as receptor for the primary response in the ammocoete larva.

these fishes; one species of dogfish, *Mustelus canis*, becomes pale by stimulation of the nervous system and dark by the output of a pituitary hormone.

Amphibia. Frogs and toads of some kind inhabit nearly every temperate and tropical part of the world, provided the climate is not too dry. They flourish particularly in the warm and steamy forests of the tropics, where brilliant light and shade and vivid colour contrasts form their natural background. Most frogs and toads show concealing, cryptic colouring in harmony with their setting, and, in such, colour change is the rule. Those kinds which are conspicuous by reason of their warning colours—black, red, yellow or orange—show little if any physiological colour change. All they do is to increase or decrease the amount of one or other of their pigments if circumstances demand.

Many of the tailed amphibia (Urodela) can modify their tone or colour as a background response. Newt larvae and the adult smooth and palmate newts are examples of this. The enhanced pigmentation which appears in newts during the breeding season is more of the nature of a fixed pattern intensified at this time. Axolotls are of interest: the white form has minute melanophores, too small to do more than change the animal from pure to less pure white. The black axolotl has permanently expanded melanophores, and prolonged residence in white tanks has no effect on this condition. The hormone of the neuro-intermediate lobe of the pituitary maintains the melanophores in a state of full expansion and if this lobe is removed the black condition ceases within twenty-four hours. The same holds good for the black skate, *Raia clavata*.

The black and orange fire salamander was the subject of Kammerar's experiments, in which he sought to demonstrate the Lamarckian theory of the inheritance of acquired characters. Salamanders which are kept for some time in black cages show increased areas of black pigment, and those kept in yellow or orange cages develop more of these colours in their skin. First the black or yellow surroundings induce expansion of the chromatophores of the same colour, then the expanded condition encourages multiplication of the chromatophores, with obvious results. Conversely, continued contraction of the chromatophores leads to a decrease of pigment and reduction of the colour areas concerned.

The salamander does not show colour change in the usual meaning of the term, but this increase of one pigment or decrease of another

* It is suggested that the hormone which causes diffusion of pigment also causes its increase, and vice versa.

is known as "morphological" colour change, in distinction to the rapid and more familiar "physiological" colour change. The distinction of terms is only a matter of convenience. Whereas the salamander can show only morphological colour change, the frog, flat fish and prawn show physiological colour change during temporary background adjustments and during darkness, but also show morphological colour change if kept for some days, or it may need weeks, on a background with some one colour predominating. The pigments of expanded chromatophores increase, those of contracted ones decrease. Prolonged existence in darkness is followed by comparable results. This clearly bears on the pallid appearance of many cave-dwelling animals.

All amphibia have epidermal and dermal melanophores and orange or yellow xanthophores; some have also an opaque white pigment which may be in movable pigment cells, but is usually in static irregular patches. In some, notably the tree frogs, a structural blue occurs, allowing for vivid green colours.

Amongst all these many kinds of frogs and toads there is no complete uniformity in the behaviour and control of the chromatophores. The pigmentary system is, to a greater or lesser extent, directly affected by light. Both melanophores and xanthophores are under hormone control, but the xanthophores may have a lower threshold of response. The dermal melanophores are the most consistent in their response, and it is these that are used in most colour-change studies.

Both the skin and the eyes act as receptors for the many stimuli which evoke colour change (see Chap. X). Responses are quicker than in elasmobranch fishes. Adjustment to a new background can be clearly seen in progress after ten minutes or so, though up to an hour may elapse before the change is striking, and its final details require several hours for completion. Two hormones produced in the pituitary gland determine the main background adaptation, the response to a dark background depending on a secretion of the *pars intermedia*, and the response to a pale background depending on a secretion of the *pars tuberalis* " or some organ whose functional activity depends on the latter ". One or other hormone is brought into play, or both in competition, according to the part of the retina of the eye which happens to be stimulated by light (see Chap. XI). The experiments and reasoning from which the action of two hormones in controlling colour change in elasmobranchs and amphibia was deduced are the work of Prof. Hogben and his collaborators.

For some years it had been known that a secretion of the posterior lobe of the pituitary gland caused expansion of the chromatophores, but what caused their contraction remained a matter for conjecture. Adrenalin will, if injected, contract the chromatophores of most animals, but there was no certainty that under natural conditions the chromatophores were really controlled by this means. Attention was turned again to the pituitary, that composite gland with so many regions and functions. Various workers held that contraction of melanophores was merely the result of withdrawal of the hormone, which, when present, caused their expansion—in other words, that one hormone was responsible for the whole colour range. More accurate observations, as regards both time and extent of colour changes, have now disproved this view. The difficulty of working with the pituitary gland is considerable, for extracts from any lobe or region cause a variety of physiological

FIG. 7.—The Melanophore Index.

results, in addition to any effect they may have on the pigment cells. The blood supply to the gland also complicates matters, for, being a portal system, traces of the secretions of any one part of the gland are usually present in any other part.

Chromatophores show many stages between complete expansion and complete contraction. A melanophore index was introduced by Hogben to permit of accurate description of these stages, taking full contraction as M 1 and full expansion as M 5. This replaces vague terms such as " partial expansion " and brings out a number of facts otherwise overlooked. It had long been known that in darkness nearly all creatures with the faculty of colour change become rather pale. Careful observation places their condition at M 3 or 2·7, an intermediate condition, and one distinct from the pale condition on a white background in daylight, where the index is M 1 or 1·5.

The most important means of tracing the course of events, and interpreting these, was, however, the timing of various colour changes and comparison of the resulting graphs. Suppose the one-hormone hypothesis to be correct. Then (a) the time taken in changing from white to black background is the time taken to eliminate the hormone W after background stimulus has subsided. Enough W hormone must be eliminated to shift the M index from 1·5 to 4·5. (b) The time taken in changing from white background to darkness is the time taken to eliminate enough hormone W to shift the M index from 1·5 to 3. Process (b) should take a noticeably shorter time. Actually it takes much longer. This apparent contradiction can be explained if we have to deal with two competing hormones. The long time taken in changing from white background to darkness is the time taken to eliminate an *excess* of W hormone over the B (black background) hormone which is produced at the same time. Other lines of evidence show that the speed of production and elimination of one of the hormones is quicker than that of the other. Graphs showing the times and characteristics of all the colour change phases for the crustacean *Ligia* may be referred to for details.* The behaviour of the chromatophores of this animal are quite comparable with those of Amphibia.

B. Nervous Control

Reptilia. It is among the lizard group that instances of colour change in reptiles occur. In the warmer parts of the world a great variety of lizards are found, including the chameleon; some are typical of forests, others of more open situations. Research has been done on a number of lizards native to America—*Phrynosoma*, the horned "toad", and various species of *Anolis*, an iguanid lizard. In the Old World, research has concentrated on the chameleon. A good deal of diversity exists in the accounts given by different workers, and it does not seem possible so far to frame any general theory which accounts for all the facts.

Some lizards have only melanophores in their skin, and their colour varies from fawn to dark brown or black during their background adaptation. Others, such as *Anolis*, have pigments which allow for several other colour effects (see Chap. III), while the chameleon has four distinct kinds of colour-producing layer in its skin. In all cases, however, it is the melanophores which are responsible, by the movement of their contents, for the visible changes. They screen, or reveal, the other pigments.

All workers agree that light and temperature play an important

* See Appendix III.

part in reptile colour change. There is no doubt that high temperatures cause pallor under experimental conditions, though to what extent this plays any significant part under natural conditions remains an open question. Chameleons cannot stand great heat, and on hot days lurk deep in the leafy shade, though there are desert lizards more hardy in this respect.

All lizards that show colour change become pale in darkness. The American types may be assumed to give the usual background adaptations, though little information is given on this topic. As regards the primary effect of light, *Anolis equestris* gives a positive result, an exception to the general rule. In this species a detached piece of skin turns brown in strong light and green in the shade, and continues this reaction for some hours if moved to and fro.

Colour Behaviour and its Mechanism in the Chameleon

The conditions under which a chameleon changes colour are as follows: it responds to the colour tone of its background, becoming pale on a pale background and dark on a dark one. If one part of the skin is more strongly lighted than another, the more lighted part becomes darker than the other. At night or in artificial darkness chameleons become quite pale; in the twilight of dawn or dusk they darken.

The first point to investigate is this great sensitivity of the skin to light. Is this a primary effect of light, uncontrolled in any way by the body as a whole? As far as the chameleon is concerned, there is no primary effect of light. Light stimulates sense cells or " dermal receptors " in the skin; from these nerves pass to the spinal cord, and from the spinal cord other nerves return to the pigment cells, making a form of reflex arc. So light falling on the skin reflexly causes expansion of the melanophores, and darkening of the colour effect.

As regards the part played by the eyes, these of course have receptors in the retina which are stimulated when light falls on them; the stimulus passes down the optic nerves, through brain and spinal cord, and by branch nerves to the melanophores. Since there are both dermal and retinal receptors, conditions exist which may result in a pulling in opposite directions—sometimes the dermal receptors will indicate " expand " while the retinal receptors indicate " contract ". When this occurs, sometimes one stimulus dominates the other, and sometimes a compromise results. A condition which prevents competition on certain occasions is this: the retinal receptors are more sensitive to light than the dermal receptors. In the dim light of dusk and dawn chameleons darken (not to the maximum extent) as the result of stimulation of the retinal receptors only. This same darkening has often been noticed in chameleons, and in other kinds of lizards, when resting on a background of any colour in weak light—for instance, on the concrete floor under a laboratory bench during the daytime. It takes light of a definitely stronger intensity to bring the dermal receptors into action.

We thus have two known trains of events which cause the melanophores to expand: (i) strong light striking the dermal receptors; (ii) weak light striking the retinal receptors. The question of background does not yet enter into the problem. Comparing this with the fact that in darkness the melanophores are contracted, we are faced with this alternative: Is the contracted state of the melanophores in darkness a state of relaxation, or are they kept in a state of tonic contraction by their nerve supply? Experiment shows the second alternative to be the correct one. In darkness the melanophores are kept in a state of contraction (comparable to tonus in plain muscle) by impulses coming through motor fibres of the autonomic system. Evidence rests mainly on the fact that the natural nerve stimulus can be copied by a suitable electric stimulus.

The expansion of melanophores must then be due to an inhibition of the sympathetic impulses. Stimulation of either dermal or retinal receptors can release the state of tonic contraction.

The chameleon's responses to varying backgrounds have now to be considered. In strong light on a dark background three separate factors all make for darkening: (i) the dermal receptors, which respond to strong light by reflexly causing expansion of melanophores; (ii) the retinal receptors, which when stimulated by even a weak light bring about a darkening of the skin; (iii) absence of reflected light; the animal is on a light-absorbing background, so that the direct light from the sky is really the only kind with which it is stimulated. Thus the dark condition of the chameleon on a dark background involves no difficult explanation.

In the case of a pale chameleon on a pale background in bright light, the first thing to notice is that it never becomes quite so pale as it would in darkness. The action of light on both skin and retina, tending to expand the melanophores, cannot be wholly overcome. Two conditions are pulling against a third: one set of sympathetic impulses tends to keep the melanophores contracted; the dermal receptors would cause them to expand; the retinal receptors, stimulated by a light-scattering background, would cause them to contract. Dermal and retinal receptors are as it were played off almost completely against each other, and the melanophores remain almost fully contracted.

It emerges, then, that each pigment cell in the chameleon is activated by nerve fibres coming from some part of the autonomic (sympathetic) nervous system. The whole range of colour behaviour is of the nature of unconscious reflex action, called into play through sensory receptors in the skin and eye. Such words *describe* what takes place, but by no means explain it. We find a system, subtle and intricate in action, very characteristic of highly organised living matter; that is all that can definitely be said.

In the chameleon, then, the only type in which the control of the pigmentary system has so far been satisfactorily worked out, the melanophores are entirely under the control of the nervous system. Humoral control, possibly by adrenalin, has been suggested for the American lizards, together with effect of temperature and primary effect of light.

The time taken for colour responses is very short, another feature that supports the probability of nerve control. A dark chameleon dropped into water at 37° C. becomes pale in 1 minute; local paling of the skin in shadow takes 2 minutes. Both the chameleon and *Anolis carolinensis* become brown in the light in 4½ minutes and green in the shade in about 20 minutes. Compare this with the hours or days taken for colour change by Amphibia and Elasmobranchs, with humoral control.

C. NERVOUS COMBINED WITH HUMORAL CONTROL

Teleosts (*Bony Fishes*). The pigments of fish consist of black-brown melanin, and a type showing all grades from red to yellow. Mixed with these and underlying them are patches of white immobile pigment. In certain fishes only the melanophores are present, with the result that they show merely a change of intensity, from white through grey to black. In fish with more variety of pigments, true colour change occurs. In addition to the rapid physiological colour change with which this chapter is mainly concerned, many fish are capable of slow morphological adjustment. Should a flat fish, for example, find itself on unusually white or yellow sand, or on shingle derived from some reddish-coloured rock, its natural outfit is not enough—it does not tone perfectly with its surroundings. But as time goes on the needed colour appears: extra pigment is made, of red, yellow, black or white, whichever is needed, and a surplus of any other removed. This was found by keeping flat fish for some weeks in aquarium tanks with floors of suitable colours, controlled by keeping others in tanks with floors of grey of the same tone or brightness.

The phenomena of colour change in bony fishes are readily understandable in the light of the evolutionary view of chromatic behaviour set out by Hogben and Landgrebe. First there is present bi-humoral control by the pituitary gland. As in amphibia and elasmobranchs, a B hormone causes expansion of melanophores, and a W hormone causes contraction. In all teleosts a nervous control is superimposed on the bi-humoral. The B hormone continues to exercise its function, but the action of the W hormone is to a greater or lesser extent replaced by that of the nervous system. Reference to the chromatic behaviour of a series of fishes will illustrate this theory.

The Eel. The eel is the only teleost at present known whose colour change is dominated by the more archaic humoral method. Its colour adjustments are decidedly slow. The expanding hormone B is built up in the posterior lobe of the pituitary and the contracting hormone W in the anterior half of the pituitary. The pituitary can be removed from eels under anæsthetic without interfering with their normal well-being. After removal of the gland, dark eels pale gradually until the melanophores are in an intermediate condition. But they still show a limited background reaction; in black tanks the melanophores are at 2·7 after 30 minutes, and in white tanks at 1·8 after 45 minutes. Clearly the melanophores have some other form of control. It was found that in eels with and without a pituitary, electric stimulation of the spinal cord rapidly caused the melanophores to contract. This and other evidence led to the conclusion that the melanophores receive a direct nerve supply. This nervous control is brought into play, like the humoral, by retinal receptors, but in normal conditions the nervous control has no significance in the chromatic behaviour (Waring).

The Stickleback (*Gasterosteus*). The adjustments to background of this fish are very rapid as far as ordinary observation goes. Within 4 minutes they pale or darken, as the case may be. But microscopic observation shows that 2 hours elapse before the melanophores finally settle down to 1·3 on a white, and 4·7 on a black background. Any chromatophore system controlled entirely by nerves should complete its effects within 5 minutes, and these slow final stages shown by the stickleback suggest humoral in addition to nervous action.

Humoral control becomes a certainty when the time taken for sticklebacks to adjust themselves to darkness is considered. When the fish are transferred from either a black or a white background into darkness, two days elapse before the melanophores reach their equilibrium condition of 2·1. Comparing all known instances of bihumoral control, it appears that whenever an animal is transferred from darkness to light, or light to darkness, hormone B is secreted or excreted. Whenever the animal is in light, then any transference from black to white background, or the reverse, is accompanied by the secretion or excretion of hormone W in amount relative to that of hormone B.

Thus the rapid background adaptations shown by this fish in light (which under control of hormone W would be far slower) have been taken over almost completely by the nervous system. Background reversal is in the main controlled by nerves, and its final stages completed by hormones, while adjustment to darkness is entirely a humoral concern.

The Salmon, and Fundulus. In the salmon background adjustment is even more rapid than it is in the stickleback, and may be considered entirely under nervous control. The fish *Fundulus* (the American minnow) has been used extensively in the study of colour change. The melanophores are wholly under nervous control. Each receives two nerve fibres, one from the sympathetic and one from the parasympathetic. The sympathetic fibres are controlled from the medulla; stimulation of these fibres contracts the melanophores. The parasympathetic fibres are controlled from the thalamencephalon, and their stimulation expands the melanophores. There are also subordinate centres in the spinal cord which assist in control.

Side by side with this complete nervous control of the melanophores, it was found that the red and yellow chromatophores, which play a very much lesser part in colour change, are devoid of any nerve supply and are expanded by a pituitary hormone, termed " infundin " by Giersburg, who discovered it.

It is clear that while hormone control can only achieve results over large areas, once nervous control is established local areas can give different responses. This makes possible the patterns formed by flat fish during their adaptations, and the versatile changes over many limited parts of the body shown by the bright fishes of coral reefs and tropical waters. If flat fishes such as plaice and flounder are placed in tanks with a background of fine gravel, or of coarse gravel, their pattern becomes suitably adjusted. Even on a chequer-board pattern of black and white their pattern will be quite a creditable copy. In these, as in other fishes, the eyes are the only receptors for stimulus from the background. The fish assumes the colours and patterns seen by its eyes. In such a case the chromatophores and their nerve supply are quite highly organised. In a sense, the fish can move certain patches of its pigment cells as it can move certain groups of muscles. But the control is through the sympathetic nervous system, is reflex in nature, and cannot be thought of as in any sense conscious or deliberate.

Phoxinus, the minnow. Here the chromatophores are controlled by the same type of nerve mechanism as in the chameleon, except that direct light does not act on dermal conceptors, but on the parietal organ.

Reptilia. In some reptiles, nervous control seems complete; but until further experiments have been made it cannot be concluded that hormones play no part. In *Anolis* adrenalin certainly assists in colour response, causing a "mottled" pattern when the animal is excited.

D. A LINK BETWEEN NERVE AND HORMONE CONTROL

It may at first seem strange that the same type of effectors—namely, melanophores—should in some vertebrates be controlled by nerves, and in others by hormones; or again that in the same animal both types of control should exist, coming into play under different conditions.

Some years ago Prof. G. H. Parker suggested the probability of a close link between the action of hormones and that of nerves on chromatophores—namely, that the nerve conveys its stimulus by secreting some material at its point of junction with the chromatophore. The actual stimulus applied to the chromatophore would then be of a chemical nature in both cases. This suggestion was based on the important discovery that the branch of the vagus nerve which supplies the heart liberates a chemical substance when stimulated. This substance has now been analysed, and is known as acetylcholine. Much evidence points to the conclusion that in vertebrates the voluntary nerves and those of the parasympathetic system all release acetylcholine at their junction with muscles, glands, pigment cells and other effectors. Nerves of the sympathetic system produce a substance which acts in a corresponding way on the effectors which they supply, and is known as sympathin. Chromatophores are not the only effectors which can be stimulated equally by hormone or by nerve. Nearly all the symptoms which accompany a state of fear or anger, depending on stimulation of plain muscle, can be produced either by adrenalin or by stimulation of sympathetic nerves.

A substance secreted by a nerve, named a neurohumor, is however quite distinct from a true hormone. At present it remains unproven whether nerves excite their effectors by chemical means or by the polarising action of ions at the separating membrane.

CHAPTER XI

SIGHT IN THE ANIMAL WORLD

It is well to remember at the outset that "eye" is a general word. Every kind of eye shows special sensitivity to light, but apart from this basic likeness the structure of eyes and the work they do differ considerably from one animal to another.

A brief *résumé* of what "seeing" means in the case of man will help us to compare this function with that of animals. Through our eyes we receive impressions of the dimness or brightness of light; for example, we say that a room is well or poorly lit, that the night is dark or not so dark. We see objects, including our own selves, together with their tones and colours, and our eyes record whether objects are stationary or in motion. Such judgements as perception of the size of objects, their distance from us and their relative movements, are largely psychological concepts, the result of the construction put by the brain on the data presented by the eyes. So it may be said that what an animal "sees" depends on the nature of its eyes, together with the structure and efficiency of its nervous system.

The protoplasm of a living cell is in itself light-sensitive. One-celled creatures such as the Amoeba show sensitivity to light by moving towards or away from it according to the degree of its brightness. The term sensitivity implies perception of a stimulus together with a response to that stimulus. We can tell that an animal perceives variations in the intensity of light only because it makes certain reactions to these. The much more highly organised fresh-water polyp, *Hydra*, moves towards the amount of light suitable to its well-being although it has no eyes and no sense cells specialised to respond to light.

Spots of pigment are present in many one-celled plants and animals. Any pigment, merely in virtue of the fact that it is coloured, absorbs certain parts of the spectrum and reflects others. A pigment spot serves to increase and localise sensitivity to light. The pigmented eye-spots of lowly forms of life are usually of carotin (known to be connected with visual purple), or melanin, which absorbs all or nearly all parts of the spectrum. Eye-spots in one-celled forms of life are not connected with any form of nervous tissue. Perhaps light acting on the pigment gives rise to slight chemical changes which give the necessary stimulus to movement.

Passing further up the animal scale, a nervous system of increasing complexity develops. Along with the nervous system appear sense cells of many kinds, specialised to respond to stimuli of touch, temperature, humidity and so on. Among these are sense cells—photo-receptors—which are especially sensitive to light. These are naturally found on the surface of the animal. Some of the most simple are merely elongated cells lining a slight circular depression in the skin. In some jelly-fish, for example, there are " eye-pits " of this kind, each sense-cell having a process which runs inwards to join the nerve net. Between these sense-cells are others which contain pigment granules. In the earthworm " light-cells " are found at the base of the skin: each contains a transparent lens-like structure which serves to concentrate light on to sensory cells.

Two distinct elements thus occur—light-absorbing pigments and light-sensitive cells—and these are found together in every type of eye, from the most simple to the most complex.

It would seem that the most basic use of the eye is to respond to variations in light intensity. Many creatures, both by land and sea, can only carry out their functions within a certain range of light. The light-sensitive eye assists them to remain within this range. It naturally follows that any one kind of eye functions best (or only) in the type of light to which its capacity is suited. The eye of some nocturnal creatures, such as owl, bat and moth, cannot see properly in bright sunlight, just as diurnal types such as the pigeon and butterfly cannot see to fly at night. Others, again, such as the cat, and certain fish, shrimps and prawns, can continue to move about during the twenty-four hours, since their eyes have ways of adjustment to extensive changes of light intensity.

INCREASING THE EFFICIENCY OF THE EYE

Considering the very small size of the eye in such creatures as the snail, jellyfish or ragworm, and the limited area it exposes to light, any device which concentrates more rays upon the sense cells is an advantage. A transparent lens, spherical or ovoid as the case may be, fulfils this need in the great majority of cases. Where, as in the eye of the cuttlefish and that of vertebrate animals, the lens is some distance in front of the sense-cells (retina), it also serves to project images of external objects upon this sensory screen.

For mechanical reasons, and accompanying an increase in efficiency, the saucer-shaped eye becomes cup-shaped, and finally spherical. The spherical form of eye seems to give the maximum efficiency. It is found in shellfish (Mollusca), for example land and sea snails and scallops, and in the cuttlefish, whose eye so nearly corresponds in structure and ability with that of the vertebrates. Many marine worms (Annelids) have well-developed spherical eyes, for example polychaetes such as *Phyllodoce*, *Nereis* and the pelagic *Tomopteris*. The vertebrate eye is uniformly of this pattern. In the great group of Arthropods, the outer surface of the compound eye is often spherical, but the organ as a whole can only very superficially be compared with that of other types.

WHAT CAN THE EYES OF ANIMALS SEE?

In jellyfish the eyes are spaced evenly around the edge of the umbrella. In structure they range from simple pits to closed spheres. While their most important function is to keep the creature at a certain depth in the water, where the light is of suitable intensity, it has been suggested that they may also assist the balancing organs in keeping the jellyfish right way up. Indeed, in small jellyfish types which do not possess such organs the eyes may be very useful in this way. If the umbrella tilts sideways, some eyes are better lighted than others, and the unequal stimulus that results calls for righting movements. The habits of the animals and the nature of their nervous system make it unlikely that the eyes are concerned in image formation.

Slugs and garden snails have an eye at the end of their feelers. The eye has a spherical lens and a retina with sense-cells and pigment. It is very sensitive to bright light, and is among the factors which keep these animals for the most part in hiding during the hours of daylight. It is probable that snails and slugs obtain a dim visual impression of objects of moderate size such as a lettuce leaf, bread crust or small stone.

In caterpillars there are groups of tiny eyes on each side of the head. These are very serviceable for telling dim from bright light. They prevent many kinds of caterpillars, especially in their young stages, from exposing themselves to danger on the upper surface of the leaf on which they feed, while directing others with warning colours or defensive hairs to well-lighted positions on stem or foliage. According to the age of the caterpillar, the eyes direct it to climb up a plant for food or down the plant to seek shelter during pupation. Caterpillars " see " objects, but only at a distance of about an inch and a half from their eyes.

Spiders have a group of small eyes (ocelli) raised slightly from the surface of the head. They are beautiful objects, seen under a microscope, each one gleaming like a tiny green bull's eye. Some spiders distinguish light and shade and moving objects at some little distance, but cannot focus clearly. Other kinds, such as the jumping spiders, have long and fairly clear eyesight. Bristowe describes how moving objects are kept in view by the jumping spider pivoting its entire cephalothorax (front part of body) from side to side or upwards in such a manner as to keep objects within the field of vision.

Shrimps and prawns have well-formed eyes of the typical compound type. They have clear vision and a colour sense. They notice movement taking place at a distance of several feet, as can be seen by the way they turn their eyes in that direction. They follow quickly and accurately any movement of hand or forceps made above the water of their bowl at feeding time. They continue to see, when daylight passes into darkness, for at least as long as the human eye is capable of telling black from white. Swimming crabs (*Portunus*) and many other kinds of stalk-eyed Crustacea have similar powers of sight.

There has been much speculation regarding the mode of vision of the compound eyes of Insects and Crustacea. They are built on an entirely different principle from the spherical, single-lens type. The compound eye consists of a large number of complete eye units (ommatidia), each like a slender elongated cone with its apex pointing inwards. Compound eyes reach their greatest development in quickly-moving insects such as bees, butterflies, dragonflies and various " flies ". Here the surface area of the eye is very large in comparison with the size of the body. The eyes are strongly convex—they " bulge "—with the result that they see fore and aft as well as to the side. Such eyes are clearly meant for large, comprehensive sight or wave-length reception.

The speed at which these insects move must be related to their type of eye. With the human eye, when travelling at comparable speed, images would all run together and be blurred. But with a large number of eye units, one group after another viewing in turn the same area, reception of the field is slowed down. The bee probably seems to itself to meander along at a comfortable rate rather than at high speed. This viewing of a wide field, together with repeated viewing of an immediate area, allows insects to gauge the position of near objects, and so avoid them if necessary. For example, flies circling under a ceiling rarely collide, neither do the quickly moving visitors clustering around a nectar feast, such as flowering privet, willow or Michaelmas daisy.

Where detailed focus is concerned, most insects are rather short-sighted. It is stated that a butterfly sees clearly only at a distance of about three feet, and the " honey guide " markings on most flowers are not easily seen except at a range of eighteen inches or so.

The rate of metabolism, or speed of living, is very rapid in insects. The speed of wing-beat in many types is far too quick for our eyes to follow. The vibrations per second of the wing are, for example, in the mosquito 260 and in the house fly about 330.

It is not surprising that insect eyes notice *movement* very well—provided that it is not too slow. When capturing a fly on a window pane, for example, it is possible to move the hand at a rate we ourselves see, but which the fly does not notice as movement Many insects have colour vision; the subject is mentioned in Chapter II. As regards the " sight " of ants and many other kinds of insects, there is probably little comparable to vision as we know it. In the Yellow Meadow Ant, for example, the head bears two compound eyes, each with about 80 ocelli, and three simple eyes. The eyes are receptors for various wave-lengths probably including infra-red, and for the wave-lengths coming from objects within their ken.

THE VERTEBRATE EYE

The general structure of the vertebrate eye is uniform throughout the Class, but there are many minor differences which make it clear that all vertebrates do not see in quite the same way.

Focus. In mammals, the lens is suspended by ligaments, to which are attached ciliary processes projecting from the ciliary body. The ciliary body is a band running round the margin of the choroid layer of the eye. Within the ciliary body are circular muscle fibres: when these contract, the ciliary processes are brought nearer together (as is the neck of a bag when its running string is tightened), and this releases the tension on the lens ligaments. The result is that the lens becomes more spherical and is in focus on near objects. When the circular muscles of the ciliary body relax, the lens ligaments are pulled on more strongly by the ciliary processes: the lens flattens, and distant objects come within focus. Fish of the shark type cannot focus at all. To see an object clearly they must swim towards it until the object comes within their focal distance. The eyes of bony fish (teleosts) are set for close sight. In the stickleback the lens is an almost perfect sphere, and there is great lateral compression about an axis passing through blind spot, lens and cornea. There is very little muscular tissue in the eye, and little if any focusing can be possible. In some teleosts, however, the lens can, with some effort (without change of shape), be drawn backwards, nearer the retina, making distant vision possible.

The focus of the lens of a frog or newt cannot be adjusted. Instead, the front part of the eye is moved forwards for close vision. This bulging of the eye, when a frog, toad or newt watches prey it is about to seize, is very noticeable.

Position. The position in which the eyes are set on the head is a matter of importance. The South African toad (*Xenopus*), which spends most of its time squatting motionless on the floor of the pond, has eyes set right on top of its head. Most other vertebrates have eyes set on the sides of the head, for example fish, rabbit and horse. The eyes bulge and the animal can see all round, but probably in a general rather than a sharply defined way. In the cat tribe, in monkeys and in owls, the eyes are at the front of the head and the animal is better able to judge the shape and position of objects. These creatures, together with man, are said to have stereoscopic sight—that is, the field of vision of the two eyes overlaps. Among Crustacea, those with stalked eyes, such as prawns and lobsters, obviously have a more precise and varied field of vision than those with sessile eyes such as the sand and pond slaters (*Ligia* and *Asellus*), and the fresh-water shrimp (*Gammarus*).

Size. There seems to be a maximum size of the eye for efficiency as compared with the size of the body. Thus large animals such as the elephant do not have correspondingly large eyes. There is also a minimum size for efficiency; some mice have eyes only the size of a pinhead, and can see only a distance of six feet.

When the eye of man is compared with that of other mammals, the iris is found to be proportionally large in the latter, and the "white" of the eye (part of the sclerotic) is not visible, or but slightly so, unless the animal rolls its eyes.

SHAPE AND SIZE OF PUPIL

There is considerable variety in the shape and size of pupil. In man and most birds it is spherical, in the predaceous cats it is vertical, while in the browsing animals such as sheep and cattle, the pupil is horizontal, perhaps aiding the wide field of vision. A peculiar condition locally known as "chain eye" sometimes occurs in cows: outside the normal pupil is a small upper and lower arc of additional pupil.

The Retina. In the nature of the retina extensive differences are found. But first a word as to its general structure. The inner part of the retina consists of several layers of neurons (nerve-cells and their processes or fibres). Next comes the layer of sense-cells, the rods and cones; in man this layer occupies about one-fifth of the thickness of the whole retina. Beneath the rods and cones, and having processes which extend among them, is a pigment-containing layer. Thus the two eye components are present—sense-cells and pigment—and to these are added a mass of neurons whose function is to carry stimuli from the sense-cells to the brain. "The electrical impulses following upon illumination are the physiological means of communication between retina and higher centres" (Prof. Granit).

In man and in the apes and monkeys there is present, opposite to the centre of the lens, rather to one side of the "blind spot" where the optic nerve leaves the eye, an area called the "yellow spot" (*macula* or *fovea centralis*). Here the sense-cells are far more numerous than in other parts of the retina. When a man looks, for example, at a tree, the eye-muscles rotate his eyeballs until the yellow spot in each is in direct line with the tree. Then he sees the tree as clearly as possible. Thus man and the primates have a specialised region of the retina which, together with stereo-scopic vision, gives them eyesight which is probably keener than that of any other mammal.

Dr. Lindsay Johnson, who studied the retina in man and various mammals, found that its colour and blood supply, also its shape and the colour of yellow and blind spots, vary considerably. He found, for example, that the retina of a dark-eyed English girl was of a general dark colour (the retina can be seen under special lighting conditions by looking through the pupil), with large blood vessels radiating from the yellow spot. In a Negro the retina was of a chocolate colour with central white spot, the blind spot a deep yellow, and both yellow and blind spots were surrounded by a conspicuous network of nerve-fibres. The seal has a brilliant pale yellow retina with green dots, and a red-brown blind spot with a green border. The African elephant has a straw-coloured retina covered with great numbers of irregular brown patches. In all the other mammals studied the retina was quite distinct.

How these differences affect the quality of impressions received by the eye is not yet known, but it seems likely that the climate and lighting conditions under which the particular mammal, or the race of men concerned, are naturally found, may be related to such differences.

In Southern Rhodesia, where the sun is an enemy rather than a friend, the eyes of the natives seem to be adapted to tropical light, being less sensitive to the large amount of ultra-violet and to the infra-red than is the case in the European. It is noticeable that the natives continue to see more clearly than we in the dim light of evening, but are comparatively blind in electric light. The art of the native is different, too, and it has been found that he does not look at a picture as we do; his eye sees first the left lower corner, travels round the edge, and then comes to the centre.

THE WORK OF SENSE-CELLS AND OF PIGMENT IN THE RETINA OF MAN'S EYE

On the retina, that thin and delicate structure, comprising in man (in both eyes combined) an area of some three square inches, evolves the work of responding to certain solar electro-magnetic waves in such a manner as to give rise to stimuli which can, by the nervous system, be transposed into impressions of light intensity, of colour and tone, and of forms of objects. What outfit is provided for work of such magnitude?

In the retina of the human eye, the sense-cells are of two types, rods and cones. The yellow spot contains only cones, but elsewhere rods are far more numerous than cones. The further the distance from the yellow spot the greater the proportion of rods, until at the edge of the retina there are scarcely any cones. Among the outer parts of the rods and cones (that is, the parts nearest the outside of the eyeball) extend pigment-containing processes from the pigment layer. Localised on the surface of the rods is the pigment known as visual purple.

Light-sensitivity. The method by which the retina responds to variations in light intensity is as follows. The rods and their associated visual purple are concerned in nocturnal and twilight vision. Visual purple accumulates during darkness and is bleached to an increasing degree by increasing light. It is concluded that the apparent brightness of any feeble source of light varies directly with the energy absorbed by the visual purple. The periphery of the retina, which receives less light than any other part, and consists mainly of rods, has the greatest sensitivity to very dim light. Hence a very faint star, for example, is best viewed sideways.

It is probable that at a light intensity below 0·1 metre-candles the cones are not stimulated at all, but " at all levels of illumination at which cones are functional it is chiefly to their activity that we owe the sensation of brightness " (Wilmer).

Colour Vision. The mechanism of colour vision has long been a subject of experiment and discussion, and may continue so. But recent methods of research have greatly increased knowledge of the physiological facts concerned. The electrical discharges given off by the retina when illuminated in various ways can be led off from nerve fibres in the retina or optic nerve. These minute discharges are amplified and recorded. In this way, and others, the sensitivity of the retina to the different wave-lengths of the spectrum has been ascertained.

Wilmer suggests that both rods and cones are concerned in colour vision, and that for any wave-length there will be a characteristic *ratio* of impulses sent out from rods and cones. The latest work of Pirenna, however, seems to establish that only the cones mediate colour vision: thus the rod-free area of the yellow spot is the best region in this respect. Young (1801) deduced on logical grounds that there are three kinds of receptors with different spectral sensi-

tivities (mediating the three primary colours). This deductio
fits in with the facts of normal colour vision. It is now reasonabl
certain that these three types of receptor are in the cone regior
though anatomical support of this postulate is not yet forthcoming

Colour-sensitive Substances. There are many colour-sensitiv
substances in the retina, and these no doubt make possible, o
augment, the action of the rods and cones. In the retina of fish
for example, there is a yellow pigment which must be blue-absorbing
Prof. Granit suggests that visual purple is the mother substance
of many of these, since its molecule " consists of a protein nucleu
serving as carrier for about 10 chromatophoric groups ". A
Dakin wrote earlier, " The protoplasm of cells which are specialise
as receptive cells for light waves is evidently modified, and probabl
contains substances which are chemically and physically altered b
light."

Images of Objects. The image of external objects is first forme
by the lens, and then projected upon the retina. Both rods an
cones pick up the wave-lengths concerned. These are transmitte
by the neurones of the retina and relayed to the optic centres i
the fore brain, where, by some unknown device, they again produc
the effect of images.

The Retina in Other Vertebrates

In the foregoing remarks we have been concerned with the humar
retina. As regards other mammals, it may be taken that eacl
class has its characteristic arrangement and relative number of rod
and cones, together with differences in pigmentation. As a genera
condition, rods predominate in the retina of nocturnal animals
and cones in those of diurnal habit.

Much work has been done on the eyes of fish. These present
as regards the retina, much less uniformity than is the case in four
footed creatures. There are at least two kinds of cones in the
retina of teleost fishes, and in some, no clear distinction betweer
rods and cones can be made at all.

Following the discovery that rods predominate in the retina o
nocturnal animals, research was made (Bayliss, Lythgoe and
Tansley) on twelve kinds of fish, some marine and some fresh
water, with a view to seeing whether there is any correlation betweer
the depth at which fishes live and the condition of their retina
Of course, the deeper they go down, the less light is available. The
dogfish, skate and conger were found to have only rods. While
all these fish go fairly deep, none go deeper than the gurnard and
dragonet, which have both rods and cones. The trout and wrasse

which both feed in shallow water by day, had no special development of cones.

When the visual purple of the twelve fish was examined, it was found in every case to have slightly different capacities for absorbing light. But there was no correlation between the absorptive capacity and the habits of the fish—those which go to the greatest depths do not have visual purple with the greatest light-absorption capacity. Such data suggest that impressions received by the retina of fishes vary according to the individual.

DEFINING THE FIELD OF VISION OF THE EYE

In animals which show colour change, a useful method is available for gaining information about the retina. According to the environment the eye " sees ", the body takes on pale, intermediate or dark shades or colours. In several animals, for instance the South African toad, *Xenopus*, this is known to be caused by the reflex liberation of two hormones, one bringing about contraction of pigment cells, the other their dispersion.

Such a happening suggests that there are two different sets of receptors in the retina. Each set, when stimulated, causes the liberation of the appropriate hormone. In the toad *Xenopus*, which lives under water, the eyes are on the top of the head. When the animal is resting on a dark background, in daylight, then light can fall only on the floor of the retina; none is reflected from the surroundings on to the sides of the retina. The floor of the retina receives " rays compressed in a cone of which the half angle is the critical angle for air and water ". The " floor elements " of the retina cause the liberation of hormone B (producing black background response), and the animal darkens in colour.

When the toad is on a white background in daylight, the whole of the retina is illuminated by light scattered in all directions from the background. When thus stimulated, the retinal elements of the sides of the eye cause the liberation of hormone W (white background) and the animal becomes pale. The exact limits of the areas occupied by the two groups of retinal receptors were established by experiment. Other experiments, using light of one wave-length only (monochromatic), show that the two groups of retinal receptors are sensitive to different wave-length ranges, the " floor " receptors being specially sensitive to the red end of the spectrum (Hogben and Slome). The eye of *Xenopus* is very suitable for study because of its fixed field of vision. That of the sand slater (*Ligia*) is suitable for the same reason, and the work of H. G. Smith in this connection was referred to earlier. (Chap. VI).

The Eye of the Stickleback (Gasterosteus)

Fishes are known to have different receptor fields in the retina for the white and black background responses. In the case of the American minnow (*Fundulus*) morphological differences are found between the two fields, and in the stickleback they are also known to be intrinsically different.

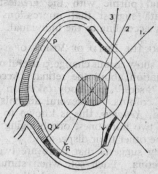

Fig. 8. The eye of the stickleback. The limits of refraction are roughly the points *P* and *R*, where the rays which graze the iris and pass through the centre of the lens strike the retina. Image formation can only take place in the zone *PR*. The zone outside *PR* can only register light and shadow.

At *Q* the critical ray through the centre of the effective lens strikes the retina. *QR* is the zone where images of terrestrial objects are formed. *PQ* is the zone where images are formed of objects under the water, including the bottom of vessel or pond.

The *B* area of the retina is made up of the zone *QR* and possibly also of the zone between *R* and the iris. The *W* area of the retina corresponds to the zone *PQ*.

In the case of the stickleback very careful work was done (Hogben and Landgrebe) on defining the limits of the retinal fields, and research led to detailed knowledge on the whole question of the mode of action of the eye. Many data of optical interest are to be found in the original paper. An unexpected discovery was that of the double nature of the lens, which has an outer " rind " of refractive index approximately equal to that of water, and a concentric spherical core about half the diameter of the whole eye, with a refractive index of about 1·5. A summary of the main information obtained about the eye is given in Fig. 8. The " sight " of the stickleback depends on the structure of the eye and its position on the head, together with the behaviour of light-rays when passing from air into water, and their behaviour when passing through the lens of the eye. This is true for any type of sight, which must depend on the structure and position of the eye and the nature of the medium in which it works.

MORPHOLOGICAL DIFFERENCES WITHIN THE COMPOUND EYE

There are Insects and Crustacea whose eyes show areas specialised for different purposes. In the Whirligig Beetle (*Gyrinus*), which swims along the surface of the pond at high speed, with half the eye above and half below the water, the eye units (*ommatidia*) of the part that sees in air differ from those that see under water. The eyes of *Ligia* have two receptor areas which control colour change, and these show morphological differences. The eyes of prawns, shrimps, and stick insects have an area which initiates distinct background responses, and will probably be found to show anatomical differences.

USING THE COMPOUND EYE BY NIGHT

The eyes of many animals can be adjusted so as to function in darkness or in light. Most kinds of marine Crustacea are active to some extent throughout the twenty-four hours. Among these, the common prawn provides an excellent opportunity for seeing the eye in its dark-adapted and light-adapted condition.

If prawns are left for an hour or so in a bowl of sea-water, with a sandy floor and in moderate light, then each eye, which at a casual glance appears to be a black knob at the end of a colourless stalk, is found to have a dark centre and a wide, clear rim of slightly yellow tint. If the same prawns are looked at with a hand torch by night, or after being kept in a light-proof box by day, then the eyes appear very black with no pale rim. Seen " head on ", each eye appears to have a large gleaming centre of pale magenta colour. The effect is the same, though on a very small scale, as that seen in darkness when a dog's or a cat's eye is caught by a beam of light. In each case the layer of reflecting pigment responsible for this effect is known as the tapetum.

Reference to Fig. 9 explains the appearance of the prawn's eye in light and in darkness. Each eye unit (*ommatidium*) has a cornea, crystalline cone and group of retinula cells. Surrounding each eye unit are two groups of pigment cells. In those nearest the outside of the eye the pigmented contents as a whole move inwards during the day, exposing the crystalline cone and much of the retinula cells. At night the pigmented contents migrate outwards and form a sheath around the crystalline cone. In the pigment cells near the back of the eye, the pigment by day surrounds the base of the retinula cells, but by night it migrates inwards, at the

same time exposing the pale reflecting tapetal pigment which has
shifted slightly forwards.

The pale rim of the prawn's eye in daylight is composed of the
numerous, almost transparent eye units, quite half of whose entire

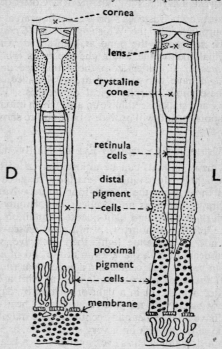

Fig. 9.—Ommatidia in day and night condition. Diagram of two units
of the compound eye. Left, in darkness; right, in light. Melanin
pigment of distal pigment cells, small dots. Melanin pigment of
proximal pigment cells, large dots. Reflecting pigment (guanin) of
tapetum, irregular white areas.

length is exposed by the inward migration of dark pigments. White
and pale yellow pigment cells remain in the rim, tinting it with
colour. At night the crystalline cone of each eye unit is sheathed
in black pigment, so that any profile view of the eye as a whole
makes it appear quite black. But when torchlight shines straight
towards the centre of the eye, in a radial direction, its rays pass
down each eye unit and are reflected back from the tapetum. Since

the pigment sheath is extremely thin, it hardly interferes at all with reflection from the tapetum, hence the effect of a big luminous " pupil " in the nocturnal eye.

The mode of functioning of the prawn's eye is thought to be as follows. In each eye unit the lens and cone cells form an image which is thrown on the sensitive retinula cells (jointly known as the rhabdome). Each eye unit forms an image of a fraction of the immediate environment. The contributions from the units combine in " mosaic vision " to form a single image. (Early photographs, taken through a compound eye, show a minute separate image formed by each eye unit, but give a false effect. When the compound eye is used *as a lens*, minute, but clear images of objects are obtained, and show the compound eye to produce a single image.)

In bright light, when the melanin pigment is closely grouped about the lower parts of the retinula cells, the amount of light reaching them is limited and concentrated, and a fairly " sharp " or well-defined image is formed. In dim light, when the pigment migrates away from, and exposes, the lower part of the retinula cells, any available light reaches the whole of this sensory region. At the same time, rays of light which enter several units can be internally refracted on to one and the same group of retinula cells. The exposure of the reflecting tapetal pigment allows light which has already passed through the retinula cells to be reflected back, thus increasing their action. All these devices combine to use to the full the dim light available at night. The image formed will be brighter but less distinct than that formed in daylight. Pigment movements are controlled by a hormone produced by the sinus gland of the eye stalk.

Work with living prawns certainly shows that they see their environment until it is too dark for the human eye to do so. To what extent they continue to " see " in darkness, by using wavelengths outside the visible spectrum, is not yet known. But it is certain that under laboratory conditions prawns retain, during darkness, the colour harmony with their background. And experienced prawn fishermen, who make their catch at night, state that prawns from pale mud and sandy bottoms come up pale, but that those from rocky bottoms with weed come up red-brown, often with bright red tails. So that it appears that the nocturnal eye can see to some extent in partial or total darkness. Several other Crustacea, for example the crayfish, have eyes which can function by day and by night.

The eyes of day-flying insects are of the " apposition " type. The sensory retinula cells are close up against the lens components of the eye unit: each eye unit is surrounded with pigment, and simple mosaic vision occurs. The eyes of night-flying insects are of the " superposition " type. The sensory cells are some distance below the lens components and the pigment is much restricted. Apposition and superposition types of eye are evidently comparable with the eye of the prawn in its day and night condition.

We must, however, refrain from too much generalisation with regard to compound eyes. Much difference in structural detail is found. Also in some insects the image formed by the eye as a whole is upright, while in others (as in ourselves) it is upside down. There is quite as much, perhaps more, difference in " eyes and what they see " among arthropods as among vertebrates.

ADJUSTMENT OF THE RETINA IN FISHES

Many fish, such as the twelve kinds referred to earlier, have been examined for the condition of the retina by day and by night. Both the sensory cells and the pigment are capable of movement. Rods or cones, or both, can move, with or without pigment migration.

Space permits no further discussion of the question of night vision, but it is evident that any animal which is not entirely confined for its movements to the daylight hours must have some means, similar to those described, for adjusting its visual apparatus.

EPILOGUE

By CHARLES STEWART

" If you look for a good speech now, you undo me:
for what I have to say is of my own making. . . ."
              King Henry IV, Part II, Epilogue.

As I have dealt with the philosophical implications in this work, any obscurities of such a nature must be put to my account.

Although the subject dealt with concerns pure natural phenomena, it raises a deep problem—the nature of " the seen ".

Charles Singer says, " It has always been recognised that Science is but a conceptual scheme which bears an uncertain relation to the percepts that it correlates. The relation of percepts to each other is, however, fixed and unaltering. When, for example, the substance with all the perceptual qualities summed up by the phrases *Hydrochloric Acid* is poured on the substance with the perceptual qualities of a *Carbonate* there follow perceptual qualities conveniently classed together under the term *Carbonic Acid Gas*. This is the sequence whatever our conceptual view of the event. It is unaltered by any atomic, ionic, electronic or other concept."—*Religion and Science*, Chas. Singer, ch. 10.

We find that percept and concept are frequently confounded with one another, and we read into the phenomena of Nature personal " wishings ". Intellectual honesty is inseparable from pure science; open-minded but cautious enquiry is essential. Any phenomena impingeing on man's consciousness are a legitimate subject for careful investigation.

Whether a phenomenon be considered natural or proclaimed supernatural; whether its reputed happening is possible, probable, or incredible, it is the work of science to examine into the matter— to record, describe, correlate, with " razor-edged " accuracy, but not to assume dogmatically in advance of full evidence. Assumption in science is of a consciously tentative nature, quite distinct from the assumption of superficial minds.

One biologist testing bees for colour-recognition showed that they did not mistake any shade of grey for blue: " In this way we have proved that they really do see blue as a colour."—H. Munro Fox, F.R.S., in *The Personality of Animals*, pp. 35–36 (Pelican Books). Maybe, but the experiment does not prove that they see blue as we do; there is no evidence that they see " Blue eyes, blue as the skies, etc." The experiments simply show that things that appear blue to us give bees a different optical sensation as compared to things that appear grey to us.

Again and again we meet knots like this in trying to gain some notion of the world as viewed by other creatures.

The authors have not been consciously either teleological or mechanistic; they have aimed at doing what true science always does—presenting the phenomena and relating it to other phenomena. They have no part with those " quarrelsome pismires " * who disprove the existence of a Divine Purposeful Mind by reference to Wöhler's alleged synthesis of urea,† or prove the same by word jugglery and misinterpretation of natural ecology. The authors admit the *production* of urea and the ecological phenomena, but humbly refrain from revealing the majestic secrets of why everything is—in fact, they do not know. Therefore when we say, " a spider mimics an ant ", " crawling in a deliberate fashion ", " imitation is employed ", the terms just convey the appearance of the matter. This book is meant for common-sense people, and not for those whose complexes compel them to talk mostly in a special jargon.

Some of the phenomena dealt with " give one to think "; to

* Pismire, Old English for gnat.
† See " Wöhler's ‘ Synthetic Urea ’ . . . a Chemical Legend," *Nature*, Vol. 153, May 20th, 1944.

attempt to explain everything in terms of present knowledge is clearly unscientific. Some departments of our colleges are unfortunately dominated by persons with such an attitude; the result is a stultified outlook in the student which tends to shut the door to advancing knowledge, or to delay the development of a wider cognition.

Interpretation of " the seen " depends very much on the stage of development of the interpreting mind, but the " seeing " itself is ruled by rigid laws. In order to see a thing, as a separate thing, it must not be smaller than half the length of the wavelengths of the light by which we are seeing it. When we have reached that point, we have reached the final limit of all our discrete vision in this direction.

It would seem that only four types of eye are possible; this is Haldane's conclusion from the data of modern physics. It is therefore not surprising that these types have been evolved, independently. There is the insect type, consisting of a bundle of tubes pointing in different directions; and types analogous to the pinhole camera, camera with lens, and reflecting telescope. But I suggest that there may be other organs which use wavelengths other than light, and " step them down " to produce images.

Finally, concerning our use of the word " animal " in regard to insects, etc., see *Dictionary of Science*, C. M. Beadnell.

" O Supreme Reason, teach me to distinguish the relationships of the details in the phenomena before me . . . that peradventure I may come to see myself truly, and not as in a glass, darkly."

GLOSSARY

Adrenalin. A hormone made in the medulla of the suprenal (or adrenal) glands, paired structures on or near the kidneys. The hormone of " fight or flight." In mammals raises blood pressure, strengthens and quickens heart-beat, causes hair to stand on end. Responsible, in man, for symptoms of " stage fright." Hormone of an endocrine gland.

Amino-acid. An acid in whose molecule a hydrogen atom of the main radicle has been replaced by an amino-group, NH_2. Often derived from fatty acids. Examples, tyrosine, tryptophane. Amino-acid molecules are the building-stones of proteins. They are soluble while protein is not, hence all proteins must be broken down into amino-acids before they can enter or leave living cells.

Antennae. Sensory processes on the head of insects; paired, jointed, usually hairy. Receptors of chemical and tactile stimuli. Organs of communication and caress, used for " conversation " in ants, butterflies and others. Sense of direction, recognition scents of species, nest, queen, etc., located in antennae of ants. Recognition of mate at long distance in moths and butterflies.

Apatetic. Protective coloration for offence or defence (Beadnell).

Aposematic. Warning coloration—black combined with red, orange or yellow; red with blue. Aposematic animals may give warning displays, do not conceal themselves, are often poisonous or have a nauseous flavour, or give off an evil smell if attacked.

Axolotl. The larval stage of the American salamander, *Amblystoma.* Usually spends whole life in water, retaining external gills and breeding. If water becomes scarce, or if fed on thyroid, can metamorphose into the terrestrial form, similar to a large newt.

Bile. An alkaline secretion of the liver, yellow-green in colour. Often temporarily held in a gall bladder. Gives suitable medium in which digestive enzymes can work and assists in emulsifying of fats.

Bioluminescence. A chemical process not confined to living organisms. Luciferin occurs within the cells and luciferase (its enzyme or oxidative catalyst) is present in the body fluids. " Cold light " occurs when luciferase activates luciferin. Production of cold light is also associated with a colloid, photogenin, and a substance which stimulates its oxidation.

Brackish water. Water partly salt and partly fresh, as for instance in an estuary.

Carbohydrates. Sugars and their condensation products: compounds of carbon, hydrogen and oxygen, the proportion of hydrogen atoms relative to oxygen atoms being always 2 : 1, as in the water molecule. Examples: glucose sugar, $C_6H_{12}O_6$, starches of general formula $C_6H_{10}O_5$.

Carotin or -ene. Yellow or orange pigment giving colour to carrot, tomato, etc. A hydrocarbon ($C_{40}H_{56}$). A constituent of chlorophyll.

Chitin (pronounced Ki-tin). Horny covering secreted by the skin of Arthropods (*e.g.* prawn, beetle, spider). May be extremely thin, colourless and transparent, or thick, coloured and very hard. May also be impregnated with calcium carbonate, becoming a " shell " such as that of a crab. Of complex composition: general formula $C_{18}H_{30}N_2O_{12}$.

Chlamydomonas. A one-celled plant which occurs in small fresh-water pools; an alga. Name from *chlamys,* Greek word for a cloak, and *monas,* single; the single chloroplast is cloak- or bowl-shaped.

Chlorophyll. The pigment which gives plants their green colour. Consists of a blue-green and a green pigment (chlorophyll *a* and *β*), a plentiful orange-red pigment, carotin, and the less plentiful yellow xanthophyll. Always contained in minute, sponge-like chloroplasts.

Chromatophore. A single cell containing pigment: several cells, each carrying a different pigment, welded into a whole. Chromatophores are richly branched. Their branches may remain distinct or link with those of neighbours. Named according to the contained pigment, *e.g.* melanophore, xanthophore. The iridocyte or guanophore contains colourless glistening bodies.

Colloid. Takes various forms: (*a*) gelatinous, *e.g.* gum, egg albumin, protoplasm. May take on a firm " gel " phase or a fluid " sol " phase. The molecules are very large and cannot pass through membranes such as cell walls. " The colloid possesses ENERGIA. It may be looked upon as the probable primary source of the force appearing in the phenomena of vitality " (Graham). (*b*) Very finely-divided particles suspended in a gas, *e.g.* tobacco smoke, or in a liquid, *e.g.* colloidal gold. Colloids are all non-crystalline. The dispersed particles carry an electric charge.

Cosmic rays. Radiant energy of extremely short wave-length and high frequency. Origin thought to be far outside the Milky Way. Of relatively enormous energy and penetrating power, *e.g.* penetrate through 16 ft. of lead at earth's surface. " Of the total radiation-energy received on earth from *all* the stars (sun excepted) one-tenth part consists of cosmic rays. Every second these cosmic rays break up 20 atoms in each cubic inch of air at earth's surface and disintegrate hundreds of thousands of atoms in our bodies " (Beadnell).

Counter-shading. Dark back grading steadily to white underside. Effect variously obtained, *e.g.* by graded tones of continuous colour, or by a pattern such as spots, which are closely set over the back and more and more spaced towards the underside. Counter-shading neutralises the effect of light on any solid object in the open, which normally makes upper parts light and lower parts dark. The animal or object with counter-shading does not stand out in relief from its environment. Reversed counter-shading is shown in animals which habitually assume an upside-down position.

Critical angle. When two media of different density (such as air and water) are in contact, rays of light are refracted in passing from one to the other. " When the angle of incidence (of light rays) from air on to a denser medium is nearly 90°, the angle of refraction is called the critical angle for that medium. The critical angle for water is 49°, for glass 42° " (Spencer White).

Cryptic. Concealing, hiding in safety, cf. crypt of church. Any colour scheme that allows its wearer to remain unobserved.

Decapod. Ten-limbed creature. (*a*) Decapod Crustacea, having ten pairs of thoracic legs, *e.g.* crayfish, prawn, crab. (*b*) Ten-armed Cephalopoda, *e.g.* cuttlefish, squid.

Dermal. Belonging to the skin, the " deep skin " or dermis of vertebrates. Dermal receptors (sense cells) occur here, also chromatophores; the latter occur also in the epidermis.

Diatom. Unicellular form of green alga (group including seaweeds). Have a cell wall impregnated with silica and often sculptured in symmetrical fashion. Marine and fresh-water types.

Disruptive coloration. (Dazzle camouflage). A colour scheme which deflects attention from the real outline of the animal or object, *e.g.* irregular patches of contrasting colours and tones, or a conspicuous broad stripe down the back or across the eye. Function, " to prevent, or to delay as long as possible, the first recognition of an animal by sight " (Cott).

Diurnal. During the daytime (contrast with nocturnal). Used of animals active only during the day, or of the opening of a flower that " sleeps " at night.

Effector. A cell or organ which does work of some kind, *e.g.* gland, pigment, or muscle cell. Most effectors do work if stimulated by nerves or by hormones which are called into play by some receptor. Example: chromatophores of chameleon are effectors called into play by dermal or by retinal receptors acting via the nervous system. Cilia, sting cells and a few kinds of chromatophores are " independent effectors " and respond directly to light, temperature and chemical stimuli.

Elasmobranch. Fishes such as skate, ray, torpedo, shark, dogfish. Skeleton of cartilage, not bone. Name from plate-like form of gill.

Elytra. The front pair of wings in insects such as beetles and some kinds of bugs. Thick, hard, and covering the folded membraneous back wings when the insect is at rest. During flight held out rigidly, at right angles to the body.

Endocrine. Endocrine gland: gland of internal secretion, *i.e.* its secretion or hormone enters the blood directly, and while traversing the whole body, causes a specific response in some organ or tissue. *See also* Adrenalin.

Enzyme. An organic agent which effects some chemical change without itself changing to any appreciable extent. A ferment or catalyst. Enzymes carry out an immense number of changes involved in the process of living. Each has a strictly limited action, and is often called after the substance on which it works, *e.g.* luciferin, luciferase. Names of ferments often end in -ase.

Fat. Fats are elaborated and stored within cells specialised for this function. Term usually applied to fatty materials in animals, while in plants they are called oils. Oil a general term for liquid, fat. Fats and oils are built almost entirely of C and H atoms, with a few atoms of oxygen. Usually contain more complex substances, some of great physiological importance. Perfumes derived from essential oils of plants.

Fathom. Nautical measurement = 6 ft.

Gonad. A general term for a gland producing germ cells.

Guanin. A colourless pigment, reflecting light and having a silver appearance. Contained in pigment cells called guanophores, leucophores or iridocytes. A waste product resulting from the breakdown of nuclear proteins.

Haemoglobin. Red pigment of vertebrates; occurs in blood cells and muscle cells. Molecule consists of a protein, globin, combined with a non-protein part called haem, in which iron is found. Haemoglobin can easily be crystallised. Combines with oxygen to form oxyhaemoglobin which easily dissociates and releases oxygen again. Haemoglobin is purple, oxyhaemoglobin is scarlet.

Hormone. A chemical messenger; a secretion released directly into the blood as it flows through certain glands, *e.g.* thyroxin from the thyroid, insulin from the pancreas.

Hymenoptera. An order of insects having two pairs of membraneous wings, *e.g.* bee, wasp, ichneumon " fly."

Hypothesis. A tentative explanation of observed phenomena.

Imago. The image or perfect form of an insect which passes through a metamorphosis during its life story.

Iridocyte. See Guanin.

Larva. The active young stage of an animal, distinct in appearance from the adult. Special names are given to well-known larvae, *e.g.* caterpillar (L. of butterfly or moth), maggot (L. of fly), leatherjacket (L. of Crane Fly), axolotl (L. of American salamander).

Light intensity. Every grade of light from darkness to brightest sunlight. Can be accurately measured by means of a photoelectric cell. Light falling on the material of this gives rise to an electric current which varies in intensity with that of the light. The amount of current is read off on a galvanometer.

Lipochrome. Fat containing a pigment, often orange or yellow.

Melanin. Black or brown pigment, sometimes tawny yellow. Made from the amino-acid tyrosine, a product of protein digestion, by the action of an enzyme tyrosinase. The reaction (with one exception) takes place in the presence of light.

Melanophore. Pigment cell containing melanin.

Mimicry. When an animal very closely resembles another living animal, to which it is not related, in colour, form and often in behaviour, this is described as mimicry. Mimicry may have protective or aggressive advantages, or both.

Mitogenetic rays. (Gurwich rays, ontogenetic rays). When plant cells divide, rays of about 2,000 Å are given off. Cell division is very rapid at the root tips of onions, and at such points the rays can be shown to affect other living matter. Also produced from muscles of frogs.

Morphological colour-change. Change in the amount and arrangement of skin pigments in accordance with a given environment. Brought about comparatively slowly. Permanent unless the environment is changed, in which case some readjustment can be made in the course of time.

Mutation. Jump, sport. Sudden appearance of plant or animal with some structural or physiological character distinct from that of parent. The mutation breeds true. Results from some change in the chromosome make-up, or in individual genes, of the cell nucleus.

Nectar. Sugary secretion of plants, usually from the flower. About 75% water, with a little cane and grape sugar; fructose often an important constituent. Contains traces of essential oils. Converted into honey by action of enzymes of bee.

Neuron. Nerve cell; cell unit from which nervous system is built. Consists of nucleated cell body with many branches. One branch may be greatly elongated as a nerve fibre.

Palp. A sensory organ characteristic of Arthropods. Paired, jointed, associated with the mouth region. Important in testing the nature of food, the texture of surfaces, and in recognition of friend, foe or mate.

Parasite. A plant or animal which gets its living from the substance of another living plant or animal.

Pelagic. Refers to open sea or ocean.

Physiological colour-change. Rapid reversible movement of pigment in cells: brought about by light, temperature, hormones, or nerve stimulus.

Pigment. A general term for any chemical material which gives a colour, including black and white, to plants and animals.

Pituitary. An endocrine gland situated under the floor of the mid-brain, having a number of distinct regions and secreting several hormones: eight are so far known. Concerned in growth, physiological cycles, calcium metabolism, colour-change, etc.

Plain muscle. Involuntary or unstriped muscle. The muscle of iris, food canal, blood vessels, reproductive system, etc. Controlled by the autonomic nervous system and by hormones. Normally in a state of " tonus ", from which it can be made to relax or contract fully.

Planarian. A small type of flat worm whose body is covered with cilia (*Turbellaria, Platyhelmia*). Marine and fresh water.

Plankton. Term introduced in connection with Scandinavian fishery research. Describes whole minute plant and animal population of surface waters of sea and lakes. Phyto- (plant) and Zoo- (animal) plankton. Constituents of plankton vary with season, and region concerned.

Preadaptation. Adaptations have usually been thought of as arising in response to some change of environment. In preadaptation, the organism is the prime mover: a change occurs, as the result of a mutation or of hydridisation. Then (*a*) the environment may change later in such a manner that the preadaptation is of advantage, or (*b*) the organism may find a new environment to which it is suited. Examples: where doubling, trebling, etc. of chromosomes occurs in plants, such plants are often more cold-resistant than their pro-genitors. During the last glacial period, tetraploid forms survived and became dominant in higher altitudes. A strain of *Daphnia* (water flea) arose by mutation under laboratory conditions and thrives best in water 6° to 8° warmer than that of the parent strain. This new race is potentially adapted to a warmer environment than that of the parent race.

Precursor. The material from which another specific compound is made, *e.g.* tyrosine, the precursor of melanin. Where the precursor or " mother substance " gives rise to a pigment, it is known as a chromogen.

Primary response (or effect). Movement of chromatophores caused directly by some action of light, the eyes not being involved. The chromatophores behave as " independent effectors."

Protein (proteid). A complex compound, always containing nitrogen. Built up from numbers of amino-acids; often in very large molecules. Essential for building and renewal of protoplasm.

Protoplasm. Living matter, always present in the form of the cell unit, with controlling nucleus and surrounding cytoplasm. A physico-chemical system involving water (¾ by weight of protoplasm), ions of salts, proteins, fats, carbohydrates and dissolved gases. In a state of perpetual change—building up and breaking down—con-serving and releasing energy.

Pseudo-aposematic. Animals with false warning colours and sometimes behaviour, *i.e.* they are really harmless and edible. (*See* Apose-matic.)

Receptor. A sense cell or special nerve ending which receives stimuli, *e.g.* touch corpuscle in skin; pressure and tension sense cell (proprio-ceptor) in muscle. A collection of sense cells is known as a sense organ.

Reflexly. " Reflexly causing a response," *e.g.* of pigment cells. Here a " reflex arc," that is, a relay series of nerve cells and nerve fibres, exists between a receptor (*e.g.* a dermal sense cell) and the pigment cell which constitutes the effector. Stimulation of the receptor auto-matically activates the effector.

Secondary response (or effect). 1. Movement of chromatophores caused by an action of light on the eye: relayed to the brain and thence (*a*) via nerves to the chromatophores, or (*b*) via nerves to an endocrine gland whose hormone activates the chromatophores. 2. Movement of chromatophores caused by hormone or nerve stimulus, called into play by the brain or by reflex arcs, as a result of some stimulus to dermal receptors.

Spectroscopic analysis (of pigments). A spectrum is thrown upon a screen and a tube containing a solution of the pigment placed in the path of the spectrum. The pigment absorbs some parts of the spectrum but allows others to pass through. Where wave-lengths are absorbed dark bands appear in the spectrum. These " absorption bands " are individual to any chemical material and allow it to be identified with certainty.

Spectrum. If a prism is held crosswise between a beam of white light and a sheet of white paper, a band of colours is projected upon the paper.

The prism has split up or dispersed the " white " light by sorting out the different wave-lengths according to the speed with which they travel through the glass of the prism. The various wave-lengths reflected from the white paper appear as the seven colours of the spectrum—red, orange, yellow, green, blue, indigo, violet.

Stereoscopic (of sight). When the two eyes make very slightly different images of the same object, which are combined in the visual centre of the brain. Allows the position of an object to be accurately judged, and, in man, gives a solid or three-dimensional impression. Name from an optical apparatus which combines two photographs of the same scene taken from slightly different angles.

Tarsus. 1. The parts of an insect's limb farthest from the body. Usually five-jointed, hairy, and ending in one or more claws. Pad often present at the tip. Besides use in locomotion the tarsus has tactile functions, and some moths " smell " with it. 2. The ankle bones in Vertebrates.

Tentacle. General term for a long moveable structure with sensory functions; also used for a long grasping organ.

Tonic (contraction). From tonus or tension. Plain or unstriped muscle is habitually in a state of partial (tonic) contraction. Two sets of nerves supply it, both belonging to the autonomic nervous system. If stimulated by one set, the muscle contracts fully; if by the other, it relaxes fully. Sympathetic and parasympathetic nerves involved.

Tyrosine. An amino-acid, a common product of protein digestion.

Xanthophyll. A yellow plant pigment, one of the constituents of chlorophyll. $C_{40}H_{56}O_{12}$.

Xanthophore. A pigment cell or chromatophore containing a yellow pigment.

BIBLIOGRAPHY

The Personality of Animals. H. Munro Fox. (Pelican Books.)

Introduction to Animal Physiology. W. P. Yapp. (Oxford University Press.)

A New Model of the Universe. P. D. Ouspensky. (Kegan Paul.)

Hormones in Invertebrates. B. Hanström (Oxford University Press.)

Adaptive Coloration in Animals. Hugh B. Cott. (Methuen.)

The Seas. F. S. Russel and C. M. Yonge. (Warne.)

Life of the Shore and Shallow Seas. D. P. Wilson. (Nicholson & Watson.)

Blue Angels and Whales. Robert Gibbings. (Pelican Special.)

Fundamentals of Biochemistry. T. R. Parsons. (Heffer.)

Camouflage in Nature. W. P. Pycraft. (Hutchinson.)

The Comity of Spiders. W. S. Bristowe. (Ray Society Monograph.)

The Animal's World. D. L. MacKinnon. (Bell.)

Elements of General Zoology. W. J. Dakin. (Oxford University Press.)

Dictionary of Scientific Terms. C. H. Beadnell. (Thinker's Library, Watts.)

Artificial Sunlight and Ultra-Violet Treatment. F. H. Humphris.

Sunspots and their Effects. Harlan True Stetson, Research Associate at Massachusetts Institute of Technology. 1937.

Evolution : the Modern Synthesis. Julian Huxley. (Allen & Unwin.)

The Causes of Evolution. J. B. S. Haldane. (Longmans.)

Geomagnetism. Chapman and Bartels. 1940.

PERIODICALS

The Pigmentary Effector System. VII. The Chromatic Function in Elasmobranch Fishes." L. Hogben. *Proc. Roy. Soc. B*, Vol. CXX, 1936.

The Pigmentary Effector System. VIII. The Dual Receptive Mechanism of the Amphibian Background Response." L. Hogben and D. Slome. *Proc. Roy. Soc., B*, 120, 1936.

The Pigmentary Effector System. IX. The Receptor Fields of the Teleostean Visual Response." L. Hogben and F. Landgrebe. *Proc. Roy. Soc., B*, Vol. 128, 1940.

The Receptive Mechanism of the Background Response in Chromatic Behaviour of Crustacea." H. G. Smith. *Proc. Roy. Soc.*, Vol. 125, 1938.

Chromatic Behaviour of Elasmobranchs." H. Waring. *Proc. Roy. Soc. B*, 839, 1938.

The Chromatic Behaviour of the Eel, *Anguilla vulgaris.*" H. Waring. *Proc. Roy. Soc. B*, 128, 1940.

Studies in Reptilian Colour Response. I. The Bionomics and Physiology of the Pigmentary Activity of the Chameleon." A. Zoond and J. Eyre. *Phil. Trans. Roy. Soc. B*, Vol. 223, 1934.

Studies in Reptilian Colour Response. II. The Rôle of Retinal and Dermal Reception in the Pigmentary Activity of the Chameleon." A. Zoond and N. A. H. Bokenham. *Jour. Exp. Biol.*, Vol. XII, No. I, 1935.

Chromatophores." G. H. Parker. *Biol. Reviews*, Vol. V, Jan. 1930.

Colour Changes in Crustaceans, especially in *Palaemonetes.*" E. B. Perkins. *Journ. Exp. Zool.*, 50, 1928.

Farbwechsel bei *Crangon vulgaris*, (etc.)." G. Koller. *Verh. Deutsch. Zool. Ges.*, 30, 1927.

The Colour-physiology of Higher Crustacea." F. W. Keeble and F. W. Gamble, B, 71, 196 and B, 198, 1903, 1904, 1905.

Colour Changes in Crustacea." E. M. Stephenson. *Nature*, Dec. 17, 1932.

Control of Chromatophores in *Leander Serratus.*" E. M. Stephenson. *Nature*, June 16, 1934.

Stellate Chromatophores in the Polychaeta." M. V. Lebour. *Nature*, Aug. 15, 1942.

Beiträge zur Physiologie der Pigmentzellen in der Fischhaut." von Frisch. *Arch. ges. Physiol.*, 138, 1911.

Grundriss der Vergleichenden Physiologie." von Buddenbrock. Berlin, 1938.

Observations on the Physiology of Colour Vision." E. N. Wilmer. *Nature*, Jan. 2, 1943; *Nature*, June 5, 1943.

A Physiological Theory of Colour Perception." Ragnar Granit. *Nature*, Jan. 2, 1943.

The Significance of Reflex Action in Colour Vision." F. Allen. *Brit. Med. Journ.*, Oct. 25, 1930.

Some New Forms of Visual Purple Found in Sea Fishes." Bayliss, Lythgoe and Tansley. *Proc. Roy. Soc. B*, Vol. CXX, 1936.

Some Curious Facts about Eyes." W. P. Pycraft. *Illus. Lond. News*, Dec. 6, 1930.

The Vertical Distribution of Plankton in the Sea." F. S. Russell. *Biol. Reviews*, Vol. II, No. 3, June 1927.

" Rods and Cones, and Thomas Young's Theory of Colour Vision
　　M. H. Pirenna.　*Nature*, Dec. 9, 1944.
" Dixippus."　H. Giersberg.　*Z. vergl. Physiol.*, 7, 1928.
" The Co-ordination of Vertebrate Melanophore Responses."　F
　　Waring.　*Biol. Reviews*, Vol. 17, 1942.
" The Habits of the Angler Fish, Lophius piscatorius L., in the Plymout
　　Aquarium."　D. P. Wilson.　*J.M.B.A.*, March, 1937.

APPENDIX I

SOLAR RADIATION, AND THE VISIBLE SPECTRUM OF THE HUMAN EYE

(*For Readers who have not studied Physics.*)

SOLAR radiation is defined as a series of electro-magnetic rays or wave
These waves may be long and slow, or short and quick.　Hence bot
" wave-length " and " frequency " need to be measured.　The slowe
waves are the infra-red, the most rapid the ultra-violet.　The gamut o
rays between the red and the violet constitutes " light," or luminou
radiant energy.　They are of the type that arouse visual sensations in th
human eye, and constitute the " visible spectrum."　Ultra-violet an
infra-red form part of the visible spectrum for certain animals.

Some heat is produced by all these wave-lengths, but especially by th
red and infra-red, which are those usually referred to as " heat " rays, o
the hot end of the spectrum.

The gamut of wave-lengths from the sun must be distinguished from th
long range of other electro-magnetic waves (used by man for variou
purposes) which are shown in a Table such as that given below.　Th
includes man-made wireless waves, together with *X*-rays and othe
which are not directly of solar origin.　Recently added to the list are th

Kind of wave.	Wave-length.	Detector.
Wireless (Hertzian)　.	20,000　metres to 5 metres.	Aerials and wireless sets.
Infra-red　.　.　.	0·04　to　0·00008 cm.	Heating effect on the skin.
Red Orange Yellow {The Green visible Blue spectrum Indigo Violet	0·00007 to 0·00004 cm.	The eye (of man).
Ultra-violet　.　.	0·000004 to 0·000002 cm.	Photographic plates and fluorescent screens coated with barium platino-cyanide or cad-mium tungstate.
X-Rays　.　.　.	0·000005 to 0·00000006 cm.	
Gamma Rays　.　.	0·000000014 to 0·0000000001 cm.	

(After A. Spencer White, *General Science Physics*, p. 240, omittin
column of frequency in kilocycles.)

exceedingly high-frequency cosmic rays, the wave-length of whose photons is estimated at 1×10^{-12} cm.

Research workers, making discoveries at different times and in different countries, have worked out their own units of measurement of wave-lengths. Thus there is the now International Angstrom Unit, which can be used as it stands or expressed in values of inches and centimetres.

In the table given, wave-lengths are expressed in metres and centimetres. In work connected with optics of the eye, a more convenient measurement is that by microns or millimicrons.

[Micron (μ) = thousandth of a mm. = 1×10^{-6} metre = 1×10^{-4} cm.] Here wave-lengths range from about 440 (violet) to 700 (red) mμ.

APPENDIX II

TABLE OF RESPIRATORY PIGMENTS.   (After Yapp.)

Pigment.	Contained metal.	Colour.		Occurrence.
		Oxygenated.	Deoxygenated.	
Haemoglobin.	Iron.	Red	Pale red.	Vertebrates.
Erythrocruorin.	,,	,,	,,	Invertebrates, *e.g.*, *Arenicola* (lug worm), *Chironomus* larva, Earthworm, *Planorbis*.
Chlorocruorin.	,,	Green.	Green.	Some Polychaetes, (Sabellid worms).
Haemerythrin.	,,	Red.	Colourless.	Some Annelids, (*Gephyrea*).
Haemocyanin.	Copper.	Blue.	,,	Most Mollusca and Arthropoda.

APPENDIX III

DEMONSTRATION OF THE TWO-HORMONE HYPOTHESIS

THE colour changes of *Ligia* depend almost entirely on the behaviour of its melanophores, so that it presents a clear case for study.

The work on *Ligia* was carried out in a dark room with a constant source of illumination. This ensured that the primary response to light did not fluctuate, and so interfere with the interpretation of the secondary effects. Small tins about 3½ inches deep and painted white or dull black inside provided the backgrounds. The slaters were observed under all the types of circumstance which evoke colour change. These are as follows:—

Transference from white to black background, and the reverse.
Transference from white background to darkness, and the reverse.
Transference from black background to darkness, and the reverse.

The melanophores of the slaters were observed and recorded at frequent intervals after transference, until a state of equilibrium was reached. Their condition was recorded by the standard melanophore index, M, in which 1 means complete contraction and 5 means complete expansion, intermediate stages being noted accordingly.* The time curves made from

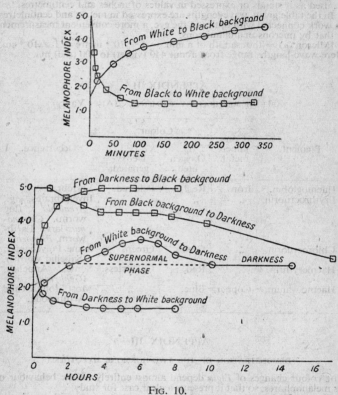

FIG. 10.

these observations are shown in Fig. 10. We see that, as in the case of the prawn, adaptation to a white background is begun and completed more quickly than adaptation to a black background. In the sea slater the difference is very marked, for animals take 2 hours to become quite

---

* With a little practice it is possible to judge the melanophore index of an animal at a glance. One or more groups of chromatophores are chosen for purposes of recording, since their behaviour varies slightly according to their position on the body.

pale but 6 hours to become quite dark. The other outstanding point is the very long time taken to settle down in darkness to the equilibrium condition of M 2·7. Pale animals take 10 hours and dark animals 20 hours for this process.

Examination of these time curves decides the question whether one or two hormones control the melanophores. Suppose one hormone W is responsible, being produced when the animal is on a white background and withheld when it is on a black ground. Then

(a) the time taken for a pale animal to darken on a black ground represents the time taken to remove W or in some way stop its action, This time, the time taken to shift the M index from 1·5 to 4·5, is 6 hours;

(b) the time taken for a pale animal to equilibrate in darkness represents the time taken to remove far less W than in (a). This time, the time taken to shift the M index from 1·5 to 2·7, is 10 hours.

The one-hormone hypothesis clearly receives no support from these results. Again, if a single hormone B is responsible, being produced only when an animal is on a dark background, then:—

Time required for a dark animal to equilibrate in darkness, namely a shift of M index from 4·5 to 2·7, is the time required to remove a limited amount of hormone B, and should be shorter than that needed for the adaptation of a dark animal to a white background, which involves shifting the M index from 4·5 to 1·5, and getting rid of a greater amount of hormone B. Actually, adaptation to darkness takes 20 hours, as compared with adaptation to a white background, which takes 2 hours. This result is even less in accord with the one-hormone hypothesis.

The second hypothesis is that two hormones are normally present at the same time, the action of one balancing that of the other. If one hormone is to predominate, then it must be produced in excess over the balanced amount. Reference to the time curves for adaptation of pale animals to a dark background and dark animals to a pale background show clear differences between the two processes and suggest that the two hormones are produced and excreted at different rates.

If this is true, then on a white background there is an excess of hormone W, and the time taken for a pale animal to equilibrate in darkness represents the time taken to remove the excess of W, namely, 10 hours. Similarly the time taken for a dark animal to equilibrate in darkness is the time taken to remove the excess of B hormone, namely 16 hours. Hormone B appears to be more slowly removed than hormone W. This is confirmed in quite a striking way in the " supernormal phase " shown during the transition from white background to darkness. Pale animals placed in darkness darken slightly until they reach the typical M index of 2·7 for darkness. They then *continue to darken*, settling down again to the 2·7 status after a further 6 hours. What happens is this. On a white background the animal produces a large amount of B and also of W, W being in sufficient excess to override B. When the white background stimulus is removed, and darkness substituted, then considerable amounts of both B and W must be eliminated before they attain their new equilibrium. W is eliminated more quickly than B, and reaches its correct amount for darkness after 2 hours. B is eliminated more slowly and does not reach its correct amount for darkness until 8 hours have elapsed. During the final 6 hours it therefore shows its presence by causing a temporary excess expansion of the melanophores.

APPENDIX IV

FROG'S COLOUR CHANGE: WHICH FACTORS OVERRIDE OTHERS WHEN ACTING IN OPPOSITION.

(After Yapp.)

1. Cold, wet, black ground.
2. Cold, dry, black ground.
3. { Hot, wet, white ground.
   { Cold, wet, white ground.
4. Hot, dry, black ground.
5. Cold, dry, white ground.
6. { Hot, wet, white ground.
   { Hot, dry, white ground.

(Cold = on ice. Hot = 20° C. Wet = saturated air. Dry = desiccated air.)

The eight possible combinations of factors are shown, arranged in order of the depth of tint which they induce. The groups bracketed together are equal in effect.

APPENDIX V

RELATIVE REFLECTION BY PIGMENTS OF THE SAME " COLOUR."

Pigment	Wave lengths in mμ							
	440	480	520	560	600	640	680	700
Tuscan red	29	29	33	33	66	83	96	100
American vermilion	12	8	10	14	37	81	100	100
Yellow ochre	31	32	49	80	100	91	90	90
Chrome yellow (medium)	6	7	22	80	97	100	100	100

(Table 8: " The Pigmentary Effector System. IX. The Receptor Fields of the Teleostean Visual Response," L. Hogben and F. Landgrebe, *Proc. Roy. Soc.*, B, Vol. 128, 1940.)

APPENDIX VI

OPTICAL EFFECT OF COLOURS AT A DISTANCE

The French tricolor was flown in 1794 with equal widths of red, white and blue colour. Owing to different degrees of visibility at a distance the amount of blue looked larger than both white and red, and the red looked less than the white.

Experiments were then made to see what proportions of the colours would give the effect of equality. The proportions fixed, for every 100 parts, were 30 parts of blue, 33 parts of white, and 37 parts of red.